An Introduction To Radioactivity

ENGLAND:	BUTTERWORTH & CO. (PUBLISHERS) LTD. LONDON: 88 Kingsway, W.C.2
AUSTRALIA:	BUTTERWORTH & CO. (AUSTRALIA) LTD. SYDNEY: 6/8 O'Connell Street MELBOURNE: 473 Bourke Street BRISBANE: 240 Queen Street
CANADA:	BUTTERWORTH & CO. (CANADA) LTD. TORONTO: 1367 Danforth Avenue, 6
NEW ZEALAND:	BUTTERWORTH & CO. (NEW ZEALAND) LTD. WELLINGTON: 49/51 Ballance Street AUCKLAND: 35 High Street
SOUTH AFRICA:	BUTTERWORTH & CO. (SOUTH AFRICA) LTD. DURBAN: 33/35 Beach Grove
U.S.A.:	BUTTERWORTH INC. WASHINGTON, D.C.: 7235 Wisconsin Avenue, 14

An Introduction To Radioactivity

ERIC NEIL JENKINS

B.Sc., M.Sc.

Formerly a Principal Scientific Officer, A.E.R.E., Harwell

LONDON

BUTTERWORTHS

1964

539.7
J415

Suggested U.D.C. number 539.16

Printed in Great Britain at the Pitman Press, Bath

CONTENTS

227411

PREFACE

THE author was trained as a chemist, and after some years of research experience in physical and inorganic chemistry began to work with radioactivity in 1950. In some ways this book represents the information which he would then have liked to have had available in a convenient form. It may be suitable as a starting point for other professional chemists, physicists and engineers who enter atomic energy or isotope laboratories for the first time, as well as for students at technical colleges and colleges of advanced technology. This book has also been influenced by a series of lecture-demonstrations on 'Radioactivity' for fifth and sixth form pupils, given by the author with various colleagues over the years 1956–1960 under the sponsorship of the Royal Institute of Chemistry and of the Royal Institution, London. The proposed syllabuses for 'O' and 'A' level Chemistry and Physics, published by John Murray for the Science Masters Association and the Association of Women Science Teachers in 1961, include a considerable amount of radiochemistry and nuclear physics, and it is hoped that this book will also be found of service as a textbook for these examinations.

The treatment of the subject matter uses the historical and occasionally the personal approach. Marie Curie said that 'In Science we must be interested in things, not in persons,' which might imply that the human interest and motivation is irrelevant. The political and social importance of scientific discovery over the half a century since her remark have prompted many to ask, with George Schuster, 'Why are we interested only in what scientists do and not in what they are?' The author is convinced that the subject of radioactivity provides ample useful starting points for general humane and cultural studies in sixth forms and technical colleges.

The author wishes to acknowledge the sympathy and secretarial help of his wife and the encouragement and fellowship of the staff and members of Wycliffe Hall, Oxford, where this book was largely written in the intervals of theological study in 1961–2. He also acknowledges his indebtedness to the source books which are listed in the 'Suggestions for further reading'.

1

INTRODUCTION

The discovery of radioactivity in 1896 was not an isolated event. The ground had first been prepared by new discoveries about matter, and by the discovery of two new physical forces, those of electricity and of electromagnetic radiation.

During the nineteenth century, chemical science had shown that matter was not continuous but was composed of tiny, individual particles, called atoms. Electricity had been studied by Benjamin Franklin and by Alessandro Volta in the eighteenth century and by Michael Faraday in the first half of the nineteenth century. Towards the end of the nineteenth century, scientists recognized that electricity also was not continuous but was made up of units. This was implied in Faraday's Laws of Electrolysis (1834) and was specifically stated by G. Johnstone Stoney in 1874. He introduced the word 'electron' in 1891 for the smallest unit of electrical charge associated with ions in aqueous solution or with gaseous ions. The term 'electron' was eventually used to denote the subatomic particles which carry one unit of negative charge, and which have a weight 1/1835th that of the lightest atom, which is that of hydrogen. Matter as a whole is electrically neutral, because the negative electrons are balanced by positive charges in the atoms. The electrons, being smaller and lighter than the atoms, are freer to move about. An excess of electrons at any spot makes a negative charge, e.g. at the negative terminal of a battery: a deficiency of electrons makes a positive charge, e.g. at the positive terminal of the battery. The materials which conduct electricity, such as copper, are those which allow the relatively free passage of electrons from negative to positive terminal outside the battery. Unfortunately, it is still conventional to say that 'electricity' flows from what is labelled as positive to negative. Franklin, a century before the electron theory, defined the electrical charge on electrified glass as positive, and that on electrified sealing-wax as negative.

Considerable research had also been carried out on the interaction of electricity with matter, particularly the study of the passage of electricity through solids, liquids and gases.

The passage of electricity through certain *solids*, e.g. metals, finds everyday application in the telegraph, telephone, domestic electricity, etc., and can be treated quite simply using Ohm's law. The passage of electricity through *liquids* gives special effects such as electrolysis which are particularly important in chemistry. The laboratory study of the passage of electricity through *gases* was perhaps the most far-reaching in its results, for it led to the discovery of the cathode rays and of the X-rays, and indirectly to that of radioactivity. [It is interesting that the discharge of electricity through certain gases (deuterium and tritium) is once more engaging the attention of many physicists, in an endeavour to harness the nuclear reaction called thermonuclear fusion—see Chapter 9.]

Because matter in the gaseous state is comparatively rarefied, an application of a given electrical field—for example the potential difference between opposite electrodes connected to a powerful battery—is spread over fewer atoms than in the case of a similar experiment with a liquid or a solid. That is, each atom of the gas has an opportunity to receive a relatively high amount of energy from the electric field which is applied to the gas. Under these drastic conditions, some of the atoms of the gas acquire a great amount of additional energy, and behave in new ways, leading to the release inside the experimental apparatus of three new kinds of *ray* (a term applied rather loosely to a fast stream of particles or waves which can be isolated in a particular direction, *Figure 1.1*). These were called cathode rays, positive rays and X-rays.

(*a*) Cathode rays were shown to be a stream of very fast-moving electrons (velocity one-tenth of that of light).

(*b*) Positive rays are positively charged atoms or molecules of the gas, stripped of one or more of their electrons and travelling at quite high speeds.

(*c*) X-rays were formed when the cathode rays struck a solid target, such as the glass wall of the vacuum tube, but especially if the target was an element towards the end of the Periodic Table, e.g. lead, tungsten. Unlike the first two rays, X-rays could to a certain extent penetrate the glass or metal walls of the experimental equipment and escape into the laboratory where they could be detected by the fluorescence which they imparted to certain crystals, e.g. of barium platinocyanide and of zinc sulphide. They were eventually classified as electromagnetic radiation, like light waves but of shorter wavelength, about 10^{-8} cm.

The cathode rays, positive rays and X-rays had all been discovered by 1895. In each case they were man-made in the laboratory in specially designed apparatus.

In 1896, Henri Becquerel (*Figure 1.2*) a professor of physics at the Ecole Polytechnique of Paris, discovered a new property of

2

matter, which he called Radioactivity. He found that certain elements possessed the power of emitting rays *spontaneously*. The rays resembled in some ways those discovered from the passage of electricity through gases, but they were emitted without the application of any external source of energy. As often happens in scientific research, Becquerel was looking for something quite different— an explanation of the luminescence of certain uranium compounds under ultra-violet light. He thought that the luminescence might

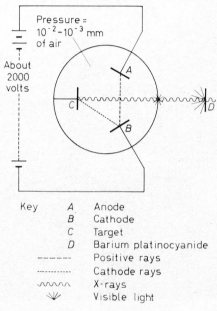

Pressure =
10^{-2}-10^{-3} mm
of air

About
2000
volts

Key   A   Anode
          B   Cathode
          C   Target
          D   Barium platinocyanide
   −−−−−   Positive rays
   ··········   Cathode rays
   ⌒⌒⌒   X-rays
   ⬇   Visible light

Figure 1.1. The passage of electricity through gases at very low pressures

be accompanied by X-rays—a plausible suggestion, for the impact of cathode rays on the walls of a vacuum tube to produce X-rays was known also to be accompanied by a luminescent glow. X-rays had been shown to affect photographic plates, so it was reasonable for Becquerel to place some crystals of his uranium compound near a photographic plate which he had wrapped in light-proof paper. As he had supposed, the subsequent treatment of the plate by developer solution revealed that it had become exposed. He probably would at first have thought that the ultra-violet radiation in the daylight was acting upon the uranium to produce (*a*) luminescence, i.e. the re-emission of light of longer wavelength, and (*b*)

3

X-rays, in the same way as cathode rays might have acted upon some uranium placed inside a vacuum tube.

As often occurs in the laboratory, a more careful experimental observation ruled out this hypothesis. He placed the uranium compound and a paper-wrapped photographic plate in a light-proof drawer. Again the plate became affected by a radiation. It is

Figure 1.2. Henri Becquerel, discoverer of radioactivity

known that the luminescence of these uranium salts rapidly disappears when they are excluded from the light. Becquerel would have expected the supposed X-rays also to be extinguished in the darkness of the drawer. Their persistence indicated that, whether they were X-rays or not, they were certainly not formed as a result of the excitation of uranium by daylight. One can easily demonstrate that (a) the photographic effect is observed with all chemical forms of the element uranium, e.g. metal, oxide, uranyl salts, whereas only the latter chemical form shows marked fluorescence under sunlight, and (b) uranyl salts kept in the dark for long periods retain their photographic power.

4

Becquerel's discovery implies that the uranium atom can spontaneously produce rays with very similar properties to those rays previously produced, under extreme laboratory conditions of high voltage and reduced pressure, in a vacuum tube.

In 1898, in another French laboratory (School of Physics and Chemistry of the City of Paris), was a young scientist who came to Paris from Poland in 1891 as Maria Sklodovskaya. Eventually she obtained her degrees in physics and in mathematics; she married a physics lecturer, Pierre Curie, and completed some research on magnetism. Marie Curie, as she became known, was not a paid research worker and she had no official laboratory. For the sheer love of discovery, and working in the corner of the store room, she started to follow up Becquerel's discovery of radioactivity. She wanted to measure accurately the intensity of the new rays. The photographic method was not accurate enough, and she used another property of the rays given off from uranium—the ionization of a gas such as air to make it into a weak conductor of electricity.

Fortunately, her husband and his brother, Jacques Curie, had invented an accurate ionization meter which responded to the tiny electrical currents of about 10^{-11} A which were produced when powdered uranium salts were placed in a shallow metal tray on the bottom electrode (*Figure 1.3*). Samples of practically every known element were examined, but only two—uranium and thorium—showed radioactivity. Her first published paper on radioactivity contained some typical results (Table 1.1) of her experiments:

Table 1.1. Radioactivity of Uranium Compounds

	Ionization current (A)
Uranium metal	24×10^{-12}
U_2O_5	27×10^{-12}
U_3O_8	18×10^{-12}
$(NH_4)_2U_2O_7$	12×10^{-12}
$UO_2(NO_3)_2 \cdot 6H_2O$	7×10^{-12}
Pitchblende (from Joachimstal)	67×10^{-12}

The radioactivity from a pure uranium compound was roughly proportional to the content of the element uranium—that is, it was an atomic and not a chemical property. The one notable exception was a crude form of uranium oxide, called pitchblende, obtained from a mine at Joachimstal in Austria. Marie Curie commented 'this fact is very remarkable and leads one to believe that these minerals may contain an element much more active than uranium'—that is, an element previously undiscovered. Basing her subsequent experiments upon this daring hypothesis, and joined now in the work by Pierre Curie, she carried out a systematic inorganic qualitative analysis of a solution of pitchblende in nitric

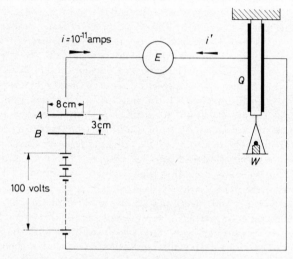

Figure 1.3. Apparatus to measure the conductivity of air under the influence of uranium compounds

Key: A and B form a parallel plate condenser; E is an electrometer, Q is a piezo-electric quartz crystal; W is a variable weight, generating current i' from the crystal

acid, using the hydrogen sulphide method of group classification familiar to generations of chemistry students.

Each precipitate in turn was dried, spread over the bottom plate of the condenser, and the radioactivity was measured. The solution of pitchblende in dilute acid was treated with hydrogen sulphide gas; uranium and traces of thorium remained in solution and the impurities, lead, bismuth, copper, arsenic and antimony, were precipitated (Group 2 of the qualitative analysis tables). The Group 2 precipitate showed strong radioactivity. Arsenic and antimony sulphides were dissolved in yellow ammonium sulphide, leaving insoluble sulphides of lead, bismuth and copper which were further separated by other reagents. The bismuth fraction showed strong radioactivity, up to 400 times that of a similar weight of uranium salt. The radioactive portion could be partially separated from bismuth—partial hydrolysis of the bismuth salts by dilution with water and precipitation of basic bismuth salts gave the greatest activity in those fractions which were first precipitated. The Curies reported 'we believe that the substance which we have extracted from pitchblende contains a previously unknown metal, related to bismuth in its analytical properties. If the existence of this new metal is confirmed, we propose to call it Polonium.'

Proceeding further with the chemical separation of the impurities in pitchblende, they 'recognized a second substance, strongly radioactive and entirely different from the first in its chemical properties: it is not precipitated by hydrogen sulphide nor by ammonium sulphide nor by ammonia; the sulphate is insoluble in water and in acids; the carbonate is insoluble in water; the chloride, though very soluble in water, is insoluble in concentrated hydrochloric acid or in alcohol—we have obtained chlorides having an activity 900 times as great as that of uranium—various reasons bring us to believe that the new radioactive substance contains a new element, to which we propose to give the name radium.' After four years of toil, Marie Curie succeeded in 1902 in preparing 0·1 g of pure radium, from one ton of residues from the pitchblende mines. Using conventional chemical methods, she determined its atomic weight to be 225 (the accepted value is now 226·096). Meanwhile, in 1899, a close friend A. Debierne, working at the Sorbonne in Paris, had discovered evidence for a third new radioactive element, actinium, in their pitchblende residues.

Detailed investigations by the Curies in Paris, and independently by Becquerel and Villard in Paris, J. J. Thomson at the Cavendish Laboratory, Cambridge, and others, into the nature of the rays given off by uranium, thorium, polonium, radium and actinium revealed three distinct types of rays. Before their exact nature was understood they were (by 1903) generally called alpha, beta and gamma rays, and these names are still used.

The radioactive power of an element persisted over long periods of time: polonium lost half its strength in about five months, but uranium, thorium and radium showed no measurable loss over this period. The release of alpha, beta or gamma rays corresponds to the steady production of energy—a further illustration of this is that concentrated samples of polonium (alpha active) and of radium (alpha, beta and gamma active) glow in a darkened room and are a few degrees centigrade hotter than their surroundings. What was the source of this apparently inexhaustible energy? Clearly, these discoveries presented a challenge both to theoretical interpretation and to further experiment. Scientists of many nations worked in their university laboratories, often with little funds and with improvised equipment—'We built our own beta and gamma ray electroscopes out of large tin cans on which were placed smaller tobacco or cigarette tins. The insulation of the electroscope leaf was made of sulphur, for we had no amber' (Otto Hahn, recalling the period 1905–6 at Montreal)—and published their results freely in the great research journals of international repute. There was little thought of commercial application and certainly no predictions of military use, though some remarks of Pierre Curie in his Nobel lecture of 1904 are interesting. 'One may also imagine that in criminal hands radium might become very dangerous, and here we may ask ourselves if humanity has anything to gain by learning the secrets of nature, if it is ripe enough to profit by them, or if this knowledge is not harmful.'

The scientists were moved to pursue their researches partly by the pure search for knowledge, and also by the discovery in 1902 that the radiations from strong sources of radium had important medical uses in the destruction of tumours. 'The Interpretation of Radium' (to use the title of a book published by Frederick Soddy, in 1909), turned out to be the key to the nature of the atom itself. In order to see how the various pieces of the scientific jig-saw finally fitted together, we must now study in some detail the nature of the alpha, beta and gamma rays and of the chemical changes which accompany them.

2

THE ALPHA PARTICLE

Within a few years of Becquerel's discovery of radioactivity, it had become generally recognized by scientists that three distinct types of radiation—the alpha, beta and gamma rays—could be emitted by radioactive bodies. The alpha rays had a limited range in air and could be stopped by thin metal foils; they produced intense ionization of the air throughout their limited range, and they were not easily deflected by magnetic or electrical fields.

The earliest method of measurement of the alpha rays used their property of intense ionization of the air. The measuring apparatus of Marie Curie (*Figure 1.3*) was of this type, and under her experimental conditions she was in fact measuring the *alpha* (rather than the beta or gamma) radioactivity of her specimens. Effectively, the parallel plate condenser used by Marie Curie was an ionization chamber. The principles of this instrument can only be understood if we first study the behaviour of alpha rays in contact with air or other gases. When a source of alpha rays, polonium for example, is placed near the electrode of a gold leaf electroscope, which has previously been charged by induction from an electrified rod (*Figure 2.1*), the gold leaves close together, showing that the electroscope has become discharged. It is very important that we should understand just why it is discharged. It is *not* due to the neutralization of the electrostatic charge on the electrode by an opposite charge conveyed in some way from the polonium. This is shown by the fact that the polonium is equally effective if it is deposited upon a metal disc which is electrically earthed. Again, the discharge is not a result of a decrease in the electrostatic charge of the electrode due to the absorption of alpha rays which directly hit it, as is shown by the fact that the polonium is equally effective if it is screened from the electrode (e.g. by thick paper) in such a way that the direct radiation is prevented. The essential hub of the experiment is that the alpha rays must be allowed to bombard the air space between the electrode and the nearest portion of the earthed metal container. The electroscope is discharged because this air gap becomes a conductor of electricity, that is, the alpha radiations have ionized the air molecules. The electrostatic charge on the electrode then leaks away to earth just as if we had touched it with an earthed wire.

So far we have assumed that the polonium was held very near to the electroscope—say within an inch of the electrode. Is it possible to discharge the electroscope at a distance, say of one foot? The alpha rays, even from a very strong source of polonium, will not act at this distance, for they have a sharply defined maximum range in air. This fact is most readily demonstrated by using a more

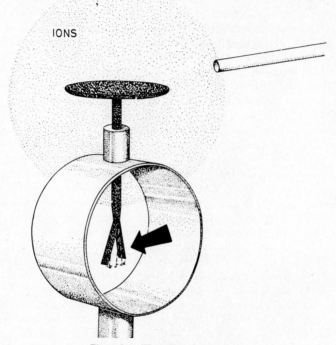

Figure 2.1. The gold leaf electroscope

sensitive means of detection, the scintillation counter. In its earliest form (the spinthariscope, due to Sir William Crookes, 1903) the alpha rays are allowed to strike a thin layer of powdered zinc sulphide, which is observed under a lens of magnification $\times$ 10 in a dark room. When the eye has become adapted to darkness, the zinc sulphide is seen to twinkle with tiny and transient points of light—the scintillations. Exposed to a sufficiently strong source of polonium the scintillations coalesce to a luminescence which is visible to the unaided eye. Much of the early research on radioactivity (including the first artificial transmutation of an atomic nucleus, by Rutherford in 1919) used the scintillation counter. The observer sat in a darkened enclosure and counted the number of scintillations per minute. His task has been greatly eased by recent developments in electronics, for by the use of a photomultiplier tube the individual scintillations can now be converted into electrical impulses (see *Figure 4.3*) and amplified so as to produce a 'click' in a loudspeaker. The rate of arrival of alpha particles at the zinc sulphide screen may be measured, either by counting each amplified electrical impulse with a scaling circuit and Post Office register, or by integrating the amplified impulses and measuring a mean current, with a ratemeter.

The range in the air of the alpha rays from polonium is easily demonstrated by bringing the zinc sulphide detector of a scintillation counter nearer and nearer to the polonium until the 'clicks' are first heard in the loudspeaker. Quite a sharp cut-off point may be determined, when the polonium is 3·7 cm from the screen. (The true range in air of the alpha rays from polonium is slightly greater, 3·95 cm, because the alpha rays require a certain minimum energy in order to cause the scintillations, i.e. we cannot by this method detect alpha rays which have been *completely* stopped by air.) Each alpha-emitting substance has its own characteristic maximum range in air (Table 2.1).

Alpha rays are completely stopped by a thickness of air greater than their maximum range. The partial withdrawal of air, for example by the evacuation of an enclosed container, greatly increases their range. This fact may be demonstrated very beautifully by inserting a sample of polonium, held upon a special support, *S*, into the centre of a round bottomed flask (*Figure 2.2*). The internal diameter of the bulb is about eight inches, and the inner surface is coated with zinc sulphide powder secured with an adhesive. When the flask is full of air, the alpha radiation from the polonium is completely stopped, by four inches of air, from striking the scintillation screen. When the flask is partially evacuated, the range of the alpha rays is extended so that they strike the screen, producing a luminescence which is clearly visible in a well-darkened room. A quantity of 10 mc of polonium is required, and the experiment is carried out, for safety, in an enclosed glovebox (*Figure 2.3*).

We have now to ask what happens when the alpha rays are stopped by a sufficient thickness of air. We have already seen from the experiment with the gold leaf electroscope that the air becomes ionized. Energy has to be expended in order to remove outer electrons from the molecules of oxygen and nitrogen, and this

11

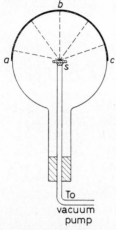

Figure 2.2. *The absorption of alpha particles by air*

a b c zinc sulphide screen

----Tracks of alpha particles in a partial vacuum

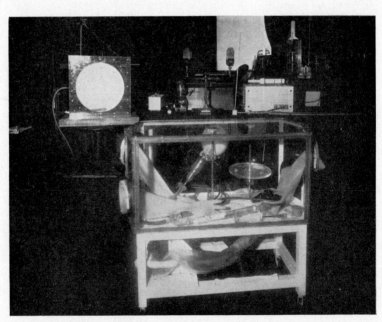

Figure 2.3. *Equipment in protective glovebox for demonstrating the absorption of alpha particles by air*

(By courtesy of the United Kingdom Atomic Energy Authority)

12

energy must be supplied by the alpha rays. Their limit of range would then coincide with the loss of all their energy.

We have still not established the nature of the alpha rays. To put the problem in another way, given that the alpha rays possess energy which is manifested, as in the ionization of air, what is the form of this energy? The observations with the scintillation counter described on p. 11, indicate a possible answer. We have

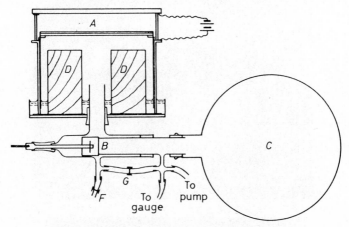

Figure 2.4. The Wilson cloud chamber

(From Rutherford, Chadwick and Ellis *Radiations from Radioactive Substances*: Cambridge University Press, London, 1930)

seen that a polonium source, which is not too strong, produces individual transient specks of light on a zinc sulphide screen—which can be amplified and discerned as 'clicks' in a loudspeaker. This suggests that the alpha rays may consist of a stream of individual particles of matter, each possessing kinetic energy. Confirmation of this hypothesis is obtained from observations with the cloud chamber due to C. T. R. Wilson. This instrument makes visible the ionization patterns produced by the alpha rays during their passage through the air. An enclosed volume of air and water vapour is suddenly expanded, e.g. by a piston *A*, controlled by a vacuum *C* and a quick-release valve *B* (*Figure 2.4*), producing a condition of supersaturation by water vapour. Tiny droplets of water condense around nuclei provided by ionized molecules of air— the previously invisible ionization tracks are made visible for a fraction of a second as vapour trails before the picture becomes blurred by the actions of gravity, evaporation and re-condensation. The ionized molecules of air are shown to lie along sharply defined

13

Figure 2.5. Tracks of alpha and beta particles in a cloud chamber. (a) Tracks of alpha particles, showing the two ranges. (b) alpha and beta tracks in hydrogen, showing the difference in ionizing power

(From Rutherford, Chadwick and Ellis *Radiations from Radioactive Substances:* Cambridge University Press, London, 1930)

14

tracks (*Figure 2.5*). The cloud chamber tracks and the individual scintillations on zinc sulphide both suggest that the alpha rays consist of streams of fast-moving particles. We shall from this point in the chapter refer to 'alpha *particles*' rather than continue to use the less definite phrase 'alpha *rays*.'

The ionization of air molecules along the track of an alpha particle represents in part a conversion of kinetic energy into electrical energy. Bearing this in mind we can re-examine the ionization chamber, used by Madame Curie as a quantitative measure of the emission of alpha particles. If each alpha particle produces a certain fixed amount of electrical energy, the total number of alpha particles per unit time which enter the chamber is proportional to the total electrical energy produced. This electrical energy may be measured by collecting the negatively and positively charged gaseous ions on parallel plate electrodes (*Figure 1.3*) with several hundred volts difference in potential, and then measuring the minute currents which flow in the external circuit. These currents are of the order of 10^{-11} A. One of the great advances in the study of radioactivity by the Curies, husband and wife, was the choice of an instrument which would measure such small currents with fair accuracy. By a remarkable coincidence, Pierre Curie had previously been working with his brother Jacques on another piece of research—into piezoelectricity, the production of small electrical charges by compression or extension of crystals, which had apparently nothing whatever to do with radioactivity but which did include the measurement of currents of the order of 10^{-11} A! He had invented and built an extremely sensitive piezoelectric galvanometer, which Marie Curie was able to use very successfully to measure the ionization currents from her parallel plate electrode chamber, when it was supplied with powdered samples of various radioactive compounds.

Today it is possible to measure even smaller currents by using valve amplifiers, so that we can record the momentary ionization current due to a single alpha particle. Such a momentary current is called a 'pulse,' and one obvious application of 'pulse amplifiers' is to make it possible to count individual pulses, e.g. as a series of deflections on a recorder (*Figure 2.6*). An even more interesting application is the measurement of the total electrical energy generated from the stopping of a single alpha particle in a suitable gas, usually argon or methane.

The ionization chamber is made sufficiently large and the electrodes placed far enough apart for all the alpha particles which enter the gas to lose all their kinetic energy by ionization of the gas, before they can strike the electrodes or the wall of the chamber.

15

The momentary ionization current from each individual alpha particle is amplified by 'linear pulse amplifiers' which preserve a constant proportionality between the primary current and the amplified current. The magnitude of the amplified current—the 'pulse height'—is measured as a peak on a recording millivoltmeter (*Figure 2.6*). The successive alpha particles from a polonium source show the same peak height, i.e. the alpha particles are mono-

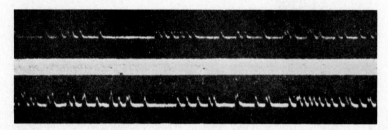

Figure 2.6. Pulses due to alpha particles entering an ionization chamber

(From Rutherford, Chadwick and Ellis *Radiations from Radioactive Substances*: Cambridge University Press, London, 1930)

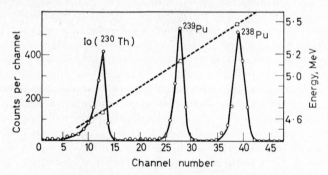

Figure 2.7. Alpha energy spectrum

(From N.N.E.S. Div. IV. Vol. 14A *The Actinide Elements*: McGraw-Hill, New York, 1954)

(By courtesy of the U.S. Atomic Energy Commission)

energetic. Other alpha-emitting elements, e.g. plutonium 239, give a different height, and yet others, e.g. thorium, give a mixture of pulses with several well-defined values for the peak heights. It is even possible, using quite complicated electronic circuits (pulse analysers) to count the number of pulses in each range of heights, and to plot an 'alpha spectrum' (*Figure 2.7*). The actual spacing of the peaks along the chart is, of course, purely relative, depending among other factors upon the degree of amplification. It is possible to calibrate the equipment with radioactive elements of known alpha spectrum, and then use it to measure the alpha energies of other elements. Because the alpha energies are so well defined, they can be measured to an accuracy of better than one part in a thousand. The usual units for measuring alpha energy are MeV (one million electron volts, corresponding to the energy acquired by a body of unit charge in falling through a field of one million volts. 1 MeV = $1\cdot6 \times 10^{-6}$ ergs). Each alpha particle from polonium, of energy $5\cdot298$ MeV, can produce $1\cdot66 \times 10^5$ ion-pairs in air. Each ion pair produced in air at 76 cm pressure and $15°$ C requires about 32 eV of energy.

Some typical values of energy and range are given in Table 2.1:

Table 2.1. Energies and Ranges of some Alpha Particles

	Energy (MeV)	Range in air (cm)
Uranium-238	4·180	2·73
Uranium-234	4·75	3·28
Plutonium-239	5·159	3·75
Polonium-210	5·298	3·95
Emanation-220	6·282	5·10
Polonium-214 (RaC)	7·680	6·97

We have discussed at considerable length the absorption of alpha particles by air or other gases. The table above shows ranges of alpha particles in air of 2·73 to 6·97 cm, corresponding to an actual weight of air of only 3·3 to 8·4 mg/cm² cross-section. This implies that it requires very little in the way of solid matter to stop an alpha particle, and this may be confirmed by placing a sheet of notepaper over a sample of polonium, when no alpha particles will be detected with the portable scintillation counter. In a similar manner, alpha particles are completely stopped by metal foil, by surgical rubber gloves, and by the thickness of glass which is usual in chemical apparatus. We shall see in a later chapter that this ease of absorption makes it fairly easy to protect laboratory workers from possible harmful biological effects due to alpha particles.

We have dealt so far with the means of measuring alpha rays and with their ionizing power. We have discovered that the so-called alpha 'rays' consist of fast moving particles, of well-defined and characteristic kinetic energy. This latter fact immediately suggests that the alpha particles from a given element—say polonium—all have the same weight and the same velocity. We are faced with the major problem—what exactly *is* an alpha particle?

A very important property of the alpha particle which made it possible to measure separately its weight and its velocity, but which we have not previously discussed, must now be revealed. Each alpha particle carries a positive electrical charge. This property was discovered by Rutherford (1903), who applied a strong magnetic field to a stream of alpha particles which were travelling through hydrogen gas along the narrow gaps between brass plates spaced half a millimetre apart. Although the deflection was only slight it was enough to bend the rays into the brass and so prevent their reception by the measuring device which was an ionization chamber. The direction of the deflection was shown to be opposite to that which was already known for the cathode rays. Since the cathode rays had already been shown to be negatively charged particles, this implies that the alpha rays are *positively* charged. The alpha rays can be deflected by electrical and magnetic fields. In either case the degree of deflection produced while an alpha particle traverses a limited width of electric or magnetic field depends upon the velocity v, the mass m and the charge e of the alpha particle. An important difference between the two types of deflection makes it possible to solve a pair of simultaneous equations for the unknown quantities e/m and v.

The force acting upon a particle of charge e in an electrical field X is Xe, independent of velocity, whereas a magnetic field H will not deflect a stationary charged particle and acts only when the charged particle has a velocity, v (analogous to a current ev flowing in the windings of an electric motor), when the deflecting force is Hev. If the deflections by the electrical and magnetic fields are small and correspond to circular arcs of radii R_1, R_2 respectively, then in each case the acceleration towards the centre of the circle is $\dfrac{v^2}{R}$ and we arrive at the simultaneous equations:

$$Xe = \frac{mv^2}{R_1} \quad \text{or} \quad e/m = \frac{v^2}{XR_1} \tag{2.1}$$

and
$$Hev = \frac{mv^2}{R_2} \quad \text{or} \quad e/m = \frac{v}{HR_2} \tag{2.2}$$

whence
$$v = \frac{R_1}{R_2} \cdot \frac{X}{H}$$

and
$$e/m = \frac{R_1 X}{R_2^2 H^2}$$

18

This principle had already been used by J. J. Thomson at Cambridge in 1897 to measure the ratio e/m for the cathode rays. Rutherford and his collaborators applied this method (from 1903 to 1914, at Montreal and later at Manchester) to the alpha particle. As early as 1903 an approximate value of $e/m = 2 \times 10^{14}$ e.s.u./g was obtained. Very accurate measurements were finally achieved by Rutherford and Robinson in 1914. They carried out two separate experiments to measure the magnetic and electrical deflections respectively, because experimental difficulties prevented the simultaneous or successive observation of the deflections within the same apparatus. It was necessary to produce a partial vacuum

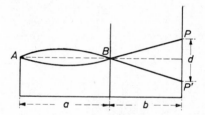

Figure 2.8. The magnetic deflection of alpha particles
(From Tolansky *Radioactive Elements*: Longmans Green, London)

inside the equipment in order to avoid the loss of kinetic energy of the alpha particle by collision with air molecules. The deflections, especially by the electric field, were small, due to the relatively high kinetic energy of an alpha particle (compared with the cathode rays of Thomson's original experiment), and in order to measure them accurately the equipment had to be a metre long. The actual means of detection was photographic—the apparatus was operated in a dark room, and the beam of alpha particles was allowed to strike a photographic plate mounted within the evacuated space. Due to their property of ionization, the alpha particles produced a latent image in the photographic emulsion, which was visible as a black spot on the plate after it was developed and fixed.

The apparatus used for the magnetic deflection experiment is shown diagrammatically in *Figure 2.8*. A small quantity of an alpha-emitting element (bismuth-214, 'radium C') was placed on the tip of a wire at A, in line with the slit B which is distance a cm from it. At a distance b cm on the other side of the slit is a photographic plate. The apparatus is evacuated and placed in a strong uniform magnetic field with the lines of force perpendicular to the plane of the paper. The magnetic field acts only over the region AB. The alpha particles, of velocity v, are deviated by the field and strike the photographic plate at a point P. The undeviated beam is shown by the dotted line. The magnetic field can be reversed after a sufficient interval of exposure, to register the point P', due to a deflection of the beam in a reversed direction. The radius of curvature, R_2, of the deflected beam within the magnetic field (cf. equation 2.2) is given

by $\qquad \dfrac{a(a + b)}{2d}$, where $d = PP'$.

For the electrical deflection experiment, the deflecting path must be longer and a correspondingly greater source strength is required. The source of alpha particles was a glass tube filled with 150 mc of radon gas (see Chapter 6), the walls of the tube being very thin to reduce absorption of alpha particles. This source is really a mixture of three different alpha-emitting elements, but including bismuth-214 which was used in the magnetic experiment. The experimental

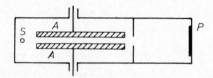

Figure 2.9. The electrical deflection of alpha particles
(From Tolansky *Radioactive Elements:* Longmans, Green London)

arrangement used by Rutherford and Robinson is shown in *Figure 2.9*. A pencil of alpha particles from the source S passes between the deflecting plates AA which are 35 cm long and only 4 mm apart, and carry a potential difference of 2,000 V. After passing through a mica slit one-sixth of a millimetre wide the particles travel 50 cm to the photographic plate at P. The whole apparatus is evacuated.

The combined results of the magnetic and electrical deflection experiments furnish a value for the ratio of e/m for the alpha particles from bismuth-214, of $1\cdot45 \times 10^{14}$ e.s.u./g. Similar experiments gave similar values for the ratio of e/m for the alpha particles emitted by a variety of elements, although the velocity, v, was characteristic of the particular element.

It remained to determine the value of e, the electrical charge on the alpha particle. This was measured by Rutherford and Geiger in 1908 and, independently, by Regener in Germany in 1909. The source must have a known rate of emission of alpha particles, measured experimentally by, for example, counting individual pulses from a small but known weight of the element in an ionization chamber. Such a calibrated source is placed in a shallow dish *R* (*Figure 2.10*) within an evacuated vessel. The dish is covered with very thin aluminium foil, which absorbs recoil atoms without causing any significant loss of alpha energy. A cone of alpha rays, defined by the aperture *B*, strikes a collecting plate *CA*. The number of alpha particles per second which reach the plate may be calculated from the emission rate of the source and the solid angle subtended by *B* at the centre of *R*. The apparatus is maintained in a strong magnetic field in order (*a*) to deflect the beta rays emitted by the source away from the collecting plate, and (*b*) to avoid escape of secondary electrons from the metal of the plate. The magnetic field is not strong enough to distort the path of the

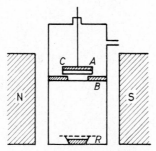

Figure 2.10. The determination of the charge on the alpha particle
(From Tolansky *Radioactive Elements:* Longmans Green, London)

alpha particles. The rate of accumulation of positive charge by collection of alpha particles on the plate *CA* is measured with an electrometer. Divided by the calculated rate of arrival of alpha particles at the plate, this gave a value for the mean positive charge on a particle, of $9 \cdot 3 \times 10^{-10}$ e.s.u., or approximately twice the numerical value of the negative charge on an electron, which is $4 \cdot 802 \times 10^{-10}$ e.s.u.

The mass of an alpha particle may now be calculated, as $e/(e/m)$ or $9 \cdot 3 \times 10^{-10}/1 \cdot 45 \times 10^{14} = 6 \cdot 4 \times 10^{-24}$ g, corresponding to an atomic weight of $3 \cdot 8$ units on the hydrogen scale (one hydrogen atom weighs $1 \cdot 67 \times 10^{-24}$ g). That is, the alpha particle has approximately the weight of a helium atom, but carries two positive charges. We now know this to be a helium atom, stripped of its two orbital electrons (Chapter 7).

This conclusion about the nature of the alpha particle had truly revolutionary consequences for chemistry. All those elements which emit alpha particles must be spontaneously transmuting themselves into another element, helium. This had already been proved for one element, radium, by Ramsay and Soddy in 1903. Again it was known that certain minerals which contained large amounts of uranium and thorium contained also an occluded gas, helium, which could be released on heating. It was still not conclusively proved that it was the alpha particle, given off in radioactive decay,

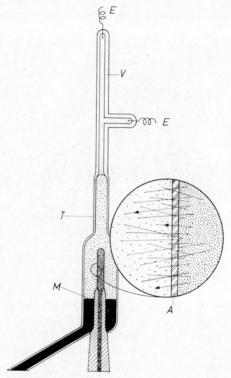

Figure 2.11. The experiment of Rutherford and Royds
Key: *A*, a thin-walled glass tube, containing radon; *T*, an evacuated outer tube; *V*, a spectrum tube; *E*, electrodes; *M*, a mercury surface

which ended up as the gas, helium. The new fact was finally confirmed by Rutherford and Royds in 1909, using the apparatus illustrated diagrammatically in *Figure 2.11*. A very thin-walled tube *A* contained the radioactive gas, radon. The glass walls were gas-tight, but sufficiently thin (about 0·001 in.) to allow of the passage of alpha particles. The construction of this container, which was the key to the whole experiment, was achieved by a highly skilled glass blower, Mr. Baumbach, at Cambridge. The alpha particles from the radon passed into the evacuated outer tube *T*, which had glass walls of normal thickness, so that the alpha particles could not escape, but would lose energy by collision with the glass and acquire electrons, becoming neutral atoms of helium. After a six day collection of alpha particles, the traces of gas in T were collected by raising a mercury surface, M, and the gas forced into an evacuated spectrum tube V, which was then sealed off by melting the glass at the constriction. A high voltage was applied across the electrodes, E, of the spectrum tube, and the luminous discharge was examined with a spectroscope. The entire spectrum of helium was identified. This spectroscopic identification showed conclusively that the alpha particles were indeed a source of the element helium.

The alpha particle is usually written in nuclear reactions (see Chapter 7, p. 72) as a helium atom, $^{4}_{2}He$, since in these reactions we are not concerned with the outer electrons.

3

THE BETA PARTICLE

The discovery of radioactivity by Becquerel was based upon the photographic effect of rays from uranium compounds, which caused the fogging of photographic plates stored inside thick paper wrappings. The alpha rays discussed in Chapter 2 have this property of producing a latent image in photographic emulsion, but we have seen that alpha particles are completely absorbed by a moderate thickness of paper. Clearly Becquerel's discovery was made possible by radiations other than the alpha rays. By 1900, Rutherford and the Curies had shown that beta rays accompanied the alpha rays from many radioactive elements, including uranium and radium, and Villard had recognized a third class, the gamma rays.

The properties of beta rays were studied by Becquerel, by the Curies and by other scientists. Most of the radioactive samples available to these early workers gave off a mixture of all three classes of radiation, and it was necessary to filter out the alpha rays with a metal foil or sheet of thick paper. The beta rays are more penetrating and their properties can fortunately be studied with relatively little interference from the most penetrating component of the mixed radiation, the gamma rays. Strong sources of *pure* beta radiation (i.e. in the absence of alpha and gamma rays) are now available from nuclear reactors, e.g. the fission-product strontium-90 (see Chapter 10).

A sample of strontium-90 will discharge a gold-leaf electroscope as previously described for the alpha-emitter, polonium. Unlike polonium, strontium-90 will discharge the electroscope over a considerable range in air—this penetrating power of the beta rays is, of course, in harmony with their ability to penetrate the paper wrappings of the photographic plates in Becquerel's experiments. Using a sensitive detector, such as a Geiger counter (p. 27), it is possible to investigate the range of beta particles in more detail. A series of aluminium absorbers is placed between the sample of strontium-90 and the counter. The strength of the beta rays is reduced to one-half by an aluminium absorber of thickness 0·074 mm (*Figure 3.1*). The maximum range of the beta particles from a sample of strontium-90 is 0·52 mm of aluminium. A small residual amount of penetrating radiation passes the aluminium, and this is due to a type of X-rays, known as bremsstrahlung, which are generated inside the absorber by the act of removing energy from, and eventually stopping, the beta rays.

The maximum range of beta rays from a given source is almost independent of the nature of the absorber, provided that the thickness of the absorbers is expressed as surface density rather than thickness, e.g. 0·52 mm of aluminium is equivalent to 140 mg/cm²

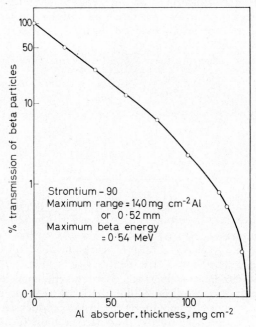

Figure 3.1. Aluminium absorption curve for beta rays

of superficial area. This density of air, Perspex or glass will represent, to a good approximation, the maximum range of the beta rays from strontium-90 in these differing absorbers. The corresponding thicknesses are listed in Table 3.1.

The beta, like the alpha, rays are stopped by a sufficient thickness of absorber because their energy is dissipated by the ionization of the molecules of the absorber by collision. Just as for alpha particles, the invisible trails of ionized molecules can be made visible in the cloud chamber (*Figure 2.5*). The beta rays consist of fast-moving particles of kinetic energy 10 or 20 per cent of that of an alpha particle. Because of the rather lower energy and much greater range of the beta particles, the ionizing events in their wake are more widely spaced than for an alpha particle, so that the cloud-chamber tracks are much thinner. The tracks show that the beta particles are scattered by collision and do not maintain a straight path. This indicates that the momentum of a beta particle is relatively low due to its very small mass.

The ionizing properties of the beta particles in passage through the air are used industrially for the removal of static electricity, for the ionized air provides a conducting path for the static to leak away to earth. For example, static electricity accumulates on the

Table 3.1. Maximum Range of Beta Particles from Strontium-90

Absorber	Maximum range (mm)
Aluminium	0·52
Air	1170
Perspex	1·3
Soda glass	0·53

woven fabrics on the looms of textile mills, and attracts dust from the air to produce a certain degree of soiling of the fabric. It is possible to expose strong radioactive sources which emit beta particles, over the pieces of finished work on the looms during the night hours when the mills are silent. A convenient type of radio-active static eliminator consists of pieces of silvered metal (*Figure 3.2*) containing the beta emitter thallium-204, which is prepared in a nuclear reactor, or else containing the fission product strontium-90.

The ionizing property of the beta particle may be used for the quantitative measurement of the strength of beta radiation from a given sample, by means of an ionization chamber. In principle, each beta particle entering the chamber produces a pulse of electricity which can be amplified and registered. In practice, two facts make the simple pulse ionization chamber (as described for alpha particles in Chapter 2) much less suitable for counting beta particles, and especially unsuitable for measuring their energies.

First, the density of ion-pairs in the wake of a beta particle is relatively low (*Figure 2.5*). This implies a weak primary pulse from the collection of the ions from a single beta particle track within a chamber of modest size. Secondly, it is found that the beta particles have a range of energies from zero up to a maximum

energy corresponding to their maximum range in air or other
absorber. Only a small fraction of the beta particles from a given
source do in fact carry the full amount of energy. This again implies
that most of the ionization pulses will be abnormally weak.

The Geiger–Müller tube (*Figure 3.3*) is an ionization chamber so
constructed and operated that the primary ionization from a single

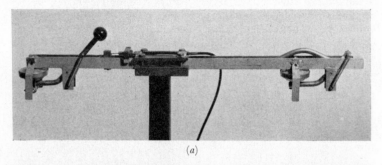

(a)

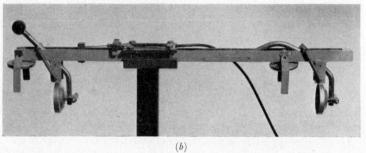

(b)

*Figure 3.2. Radioactive sources for a static eliminator. (a) Shielded position;
(b) operating position. (Each source contains 6 mc of strontium-90 in silver foil)*

(By courtesy of the Cotton, Silk and Man-Made Fibres Association)

beta particle triggers off a greatly amplified electrical discharge
lasting about 10^{-4} sec within the chamber. The magnitude of
the discharge is independent of the strength or feebleness of the
'trigger.' Incidentally, the Geiger–Müller tube is equally effective
in counting alpha particles, provided they are released inside the
chamber or the walls of the chamber, and are sufficiently thin to
allow the alpha particles from an exterior source to penetrate them.

The amplification of the primary ionizations inside the Geiger-
Müller tube is achieved by accelerating the primary ions by an
electrical field of one or two thousand volts. The fast-moving ions
then cause secondary ionization by collisions. The nature of the

gas in the counter (commonly argon at a total pressure of a tenth of an atmosphere) and the geometrical design of the electrodes is such that, beyond a critical minimum value of applied potential, the secondary, tertiary and subsequent ionizations constitute an ionic avalanche which approximates to a continuous gaseous discharge. This would continue indefinitely unless stopped by a device in the external electronic circuits which automatically reduces the applied potential. A similar 'quenching' of the discharge can also be achieved by including a proportion of suitable polyatomic gases, such as ethyl alcohol, in the chamber. The molecules of such gases are able to absorb the kinetic energy of collision by increasing the

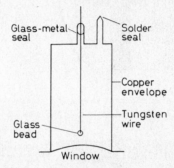

Figure 3.3. A Geiger–Müller tube (end window)

amplitude of vibrations of the chemical bonds linking the component atoms, rather than by the ionization of these atoms.

In Becquerel's early work, the beta particles were discovered to be deflected by a magnetic field—this can be shown much more readily than for the alpha particle, and can in fact be shown in a simple lecture demonstration. A sample of strontium-90 is contained in a thick-walled Perspex box provided with a vertical aperture 5 mm in diameter and aligned directly over the source (*Figure 3.4*). A thin-walled Geiger tube is supported at a height of about one foot, vertically over the aperture. The tube may be wrapped in $\frac{1}{4}$ in. lead sheet except for a 1 in. square 'window.' The discharge pulses from the Geiger tube are amplified electronically and fed to a ratemeter, in which the integrated current is displayed on a projection milliammeter or on a milliammeter fitted with a very large scale. The equipment is adjusted to provide a full-scale current when the strontium-90 source is vertically beneath the window of the Geiger tube. A powerful bar magnet is now brought up with its North pole near the vertical aperture in the Perspex box. The

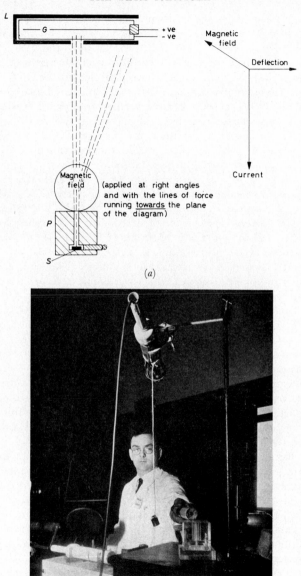

(a)

(b)

Figure 3.4. A demonstration of the magnetic deflection of beta particles. (a) *Diagrammatic representation* (Key: S is a beta active source, e.g. ^{90}Sr or ^{32}P; P is a Perspex holder; G is a glass-walled Geiger–Müller tube; L is a lead shield); (b) *the author demonstrating at a schools lecture*

(By courtesy of the United Kingdom Atomic Energy Authority)

current measured by the milliammeter is greatly reduced, due to the deflection of the beam of beta particles. By moving the Geiger tube, or more conveniently by moving the Perspex box and magnet, until the original current is largely restored, it can be shown that the beta particles are deflected to the right by the magnetic field (*Figure 3.4*). By the application of Fleming's Left-hand Rule we can deduce that the beam of beta particles is equivalent to the passage of an electrical current in a wire from top to bottom of the diagram, or else to the passage of negative particles from bottom to top. In other words, the experiment shows that the beta particles are negatively charged.

This conclusion was also reached by Pierre and Marie Curie from experiments in which a beam of beta particles was allowed to strike a lead plate, in which they are absorbed. The radioactive source was covered with a thin metal foil to trap alpha particles, the source and the plate were surrounded by an insulating medium (e.g. paraffin wax) and contained inside a metal box which was electrically earthed to avoid leakage of charge. The lead plate was connected to an electroscope, which was found to record a negative charge. In principle, this equipment could be used to measure the actual value of the negative charge on an individual beta particle (cf. a similar measurement for alpha particles, p. 20). A very accurate measurement of the charge was made by Y. Beers at Princeton University in 1943. The charge was found to be the same as the charge on an electron: $4 \cdot 80 \times 10^{-10}$ e.s.u.

The values of the charge/mass ratio, e/m, and of the velocity, v, of beta particles were measured from the observed deviations of beta particles in magnetic and electric fields—in fact this work, performed first by Becquerel and then more accurately by Kaufmann, *preceded* the corresponding measurements on the alpha particle which we have already discussed in detail in Chapter 2. Because the beta particles are more readily deflected than the alpha, both by magnetic and by electric fields, it was possible to combine both deflections in one apparatus, a horizontal deflection due to the electrical field and a vertical deflection due to the magnetic field. The position of the resultant beam was recorded photographically. If a similar experiment had been possible with alpha particles, the deflected beam would have struck the photographic film in one spot, corresponding to the resultant of the vertical and horizontal deflections. The result of Kaufmann's deflection experiments on beta particles, however, was a curve upon the photographic paper. This implies that either e/m or v, or both, are not constant for every beta particle from a particular radioactive source. The fundamental

equations for the deflection by a magnetic and by an electric field
(p. 18) can be applied to any point on the curve, and this mathematical analysis of the curve, taking m as the mass of the particle
at rest or at low speeds, reveals (*a*) that the ratio e/m is constant,
and identical with the ratio e/m for an electron (corrections must
be applied to allow for the apparent increase in m at high velocities,
as calculated by Einstein's Special Theory of Relativity); (*b*) that
the velocity v is extremely high, comparable with the velocity
of light; and (*c*) that it varies continuously over a certain range,

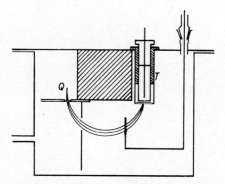

Figure 3.5. Chadwick's apparatus for the measurement of the beta ray spectrum
(From Rutherford, Chadwick and Ellis *Radiations from Radioactive Substances:* Cambridge
University Press, London, 1930)

i.e. the beta particles are *not* mono-energetic like the alpha particles,
but show a range of kinetic energies up to a certain maximum value.

The distribution of kinetic energy amongst individual beta particles is better studied with apparatus designed by Chadwick in
1914 (*Figure 3.5*). A source Q in an evacuated box emits a stream
of beta particles, which is deflected into the Geiger tube T, by a
uniform magnetic field applied in a direction perpendicular to the
plane of the diagram. Those beta particles which have the same
momentum, mv, are deflected through circular paths with the same
radius $R_2 (Hev = mv^2/R_2$ or $mv = He . R_2)$ and enter the Geiger
tube through its end window. The Geiger tube is shielded from
direct radiation by a lead screen. The intensity of the uniform
magnetic field can be measured and varied in a series of steps.
The flux of beta particles entering the Geiger tube is recorded
for each value of the magnetic field. The results may be expressed
as a graph of the relative number of beta particles against kinetic
energy (*Figure 3.6*), that is, a beta particle energy spectrum.

The simplest beta spectra consist of a number of sharp lines, due to secondary effects, superimposed upon a continuous energy distribution which terminates at a maximum value. It is this maximum value of the energy of beta particles from a particular source which determines their maximum range in an absorber (*Figure 3.1.*). Unlike a beam of alpha particles, which are all of the same energy, a beam of beta particles includes many particles which have much less than the maximum energy. It can be shown that in order to

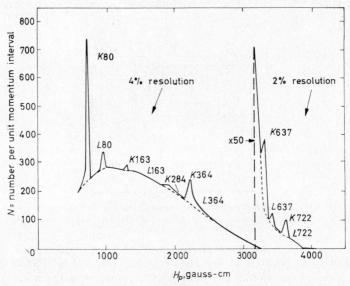

Figure 3.6. A beta ray spectrum of iodine-131

(From *Beta and Gamma Ray Spectroscopy* (Ed. Siegbahn): North Holland, Amsterdam, 1955)

maintain the conservation of energy, each beta particle emitted by a particular source ought to have this maximum value (as some radioactive isotopes emit several distinct groups of beta particles, this remark applies strictly only to those particles *within* a given group). For example, in the case of the beta emitter, strontium-90, each beta particle that is emitted should have a range in aluminium of 0·52 mm and an energy of 0·54 MeV.

In order to account for the apparent loss of kinetic energy on the part of most of the beta particles, Pauli in 1931 postulated that a new particle, which in 1934 acquired the name of 'neutrino,' accompanies the beta particle in radioactive decay. The new particle was assumed to be electrically neutral and to have an extremely small mass, small even compared with that of the electron. The difference between the maximum kinetic energy and the lower value for some beta particles is given by the kinetic energy of neutrinos with a range of velocities. Because of the lack of electrical charge and extremely low mass, the neutrino escapes from any experimental equipment, and even passes through the concrete shielding of a nuclear reactor (see Chapter 9). Any energy which is emitted from nuclear reactions in the form of the kinetic energy of neutrinos is radiated into the universe at large. There remains a finite but extremely low probability of the capture of a neutrino by a proton:

$$\text{Neutrino} + {}^{1}_{1}\text{H} \rightarrow {}^{1}_{0}n + \beta^{+}$$

The proton is converted into a neutron (see p. 92) and a positron (see p. 91). This reaction was in fact detected by C. L. Cowan and F. Reines of the Los Alamos Scientific Laboratory in 1953–56. They made use of the intense flux of neutrinos near a nuclear reactor, associated with the beta decay of the fission products. With a flux of 10^{17} neutrinos per sec passing into half a ton of water, about three neutrino captures were detected per hour.

The neutrino hypothesis may be treated by advanced wave mechanics to account satisfactorily for the shape of the 'continuum' in the energy spectra of beta disintegration. The sharp 'lines' which stand out above the 'continuum' are due to the ejection, by gamma rays leaving the nucleus, of mono-energetic electrons from orbital electron shells (Chapter 7) close to the nucleus, mainly the K shell. This process is known as the 'internal conversion' of a gamma ray. It resembles the ejection of an orbital electron from an atom, by a gamma ray which is generated externally (p. 37). The 'internal conversion' lines are sharply defined because they do *not* arise in the nucleus itself—neutrino production is not possible in this case. Two further consequences of 'internal conversion' should be mentioned: (*a*) certain radioactive isotopes appear to emit more than one beta particle per disintegration, because the beta particles from the nucleus are supplemented by the conversion electrons (p. 44); (*b*) following the expulsion of the orbital electron by the gamma ray, the vacant orbital energy level will quickly become filled by the capture of a 'stray' electron. When this happens, energy is released in the form of electromagnetic radiation, to give an X-ray which is of a wavelength characteristic of the particular element (see p. 70), that is of the element which is the *product* of the emission of a beta particle from the radioactive isotope.

33

THE GAMMA RAYS

We have seen that alpha and beta rays were distinguished amongst the radiations emitted by certain radioactive elements, by their relative susceptibility to absorption and deviation. Alpha rays are easily absorbed, but are not readily deviated by electrical or magnetic fields. Beta rays are easily deviated in this way, but show a relatively high penetrating power through absorbers. The third type, discovered by P. Villard (1900), and later called 'gamma rays', cannot be deflected by a magnetic field *and* have great penetration. The penetrating radiation or 'gamma rays' could be detected by any of the methods which were already in use for alpha and beta rays, although the response from a given weight of radioactive sample was in every case much weaker. The gamma rays will discharge an electroscope, produce a succession of discharges in a Geiger tube, blacken a photographic film, and produce a luminescence in certain crystals.

Unlike the alpha and beta rays, the gamma rays show no deflection under the most powerful electric or magnetic fields, that is, they are not charged particles. It was already known that in the discharge of electricity through gas under a partial vacuum, three types of radiation were released (Chapter 1), cathode rays, positive rays and X-rays.

Since the alpha and beta rays released spontaneously from radium and similar substances have properties related to the first and second groups listed above, it was natural to test if the gamma rays were related to the third group, the X-rays. The X-rays had been proved by Laue, Friedrich and Knipping (1912) to be electromagnetic radiation using the orderly pattern of atoms in a crystal of zinc sulphide as a diffraction grating. The essential feature in this demonstration of the wave nature of an unknown radiation is the property of waves reflected from a series of centres, e.g. atoms in a crystal, to reinforce or to cancel out one another according to whether they are in phase or out of phase, and so to form patterns of stationary waves which can be detected on a suitable screen. The work on X-ray diffraction by crystals was later refined by W. L. Bragg, so that it became possible to measure the actual wavelengths.

Rutherford and Andrade in 1914 applied this method to the gamma rays, and were able to record diffraction patterns on a photographic plate. Mathematical analysis of the data revealed that the gamma rays are of even shorter wavelength than the X-rays, and that a radioactive element emits a considerable series of individual mono-energetic gamma radiations—its characteristic gamma spectrum. Typical wavelengths lie in the region 0·01 to 1 Ångström units (10^{-10} to 10^{-8} cm) corresponding to photon energies of 1·24 MeV to 0·012 MeV.

The penetrating power of the gamma radiation enables those radioactive materials which emit these rays to be detected with, for example, a Geiger counter, at a considerable distance and through moderate thicknesses of earth, wood, brick, pipework, etc. This leads to several important industrial applications of gamma emitters. The site of a blockage in buried drains or industrial pipework can be detected if a movable plug containing a sample of the gamma-emitting radioactive isotope cobalt-60 is forced along the pipe under pressure until it becomes held up at the obstruction. The position may then be detected by measurement of the optimum response of a portable Geiger counter carried above ground. Again, the slow wearing away of the linings of a blast furnace can be followed by measurements of the radioactivity outside the furnace walls, from a series of small pellets containing cobalt-60 and implanted in the lining. The radiation intensity decreases in a series of steps, as successive pellets become exposed on the inside of the lining and melt into the furnace. The quantities of radioactivity required are very small and do not present any hazard to subsequent users of the metal.

Although the gamma rays were first detected outside absorbers which were sufficiently thick to stop all alpha and beta rays, they are not completely unaffected by such absorbers. A mono-energetic beam of gamma rays of energy 1 MeV loses 90 per cent of its intensity as measured by ionizing power, on passage through one inch of lead. A further inch of lead reduces the residual intensity by another factor of ten; that is, the negative logarithm of the intensity is proportional to the thickness of the absorber. The constant of proportionality depends upon the wavelengths of the gamma rays and upon the nature of the absorber. Gamma rays of relatively long wavelengths (low energy) are absorbed most readily. The best absorbers, weight for weight, are materials of high atomic number, e.g. tungsten, lead and uranium metals. Lead, in particular, is commonly used in the construction of 'radiation shields' for the safe handling of large amounts of gamma-emitting radioactive material, e.g. in atomic laboratories and in hospitals.

Lead and other heavy materials can be replaced as shielding material by concrete, earth or water where there is no objection to an increased thickness, which makes up for the low density and low atomic number. Concrete shielding is used on a very large scale around the more highly radioactive sections of the chemical plant for the treatment of the spent nuclear fuel from nuclear reactors.

A rather detailed study of the mechanisms by which gamma rays are absorbed in matter is rewarding, and throws light upon the processes such as ionization and scintillation counting by which they are usually measured. It will be necessary to take for granted some of the ideas of atomic structure, e.g. the orbital electrons, which are discussed in Chapter 7.

In the case of the alpha and the beta particles, it is possible to visualize their absorption in appropriate thicknesses of matter as due to a gradual loss of the kinetic energy of the particles by successive collisions with the outer electrons of the atoms in the absorber, some of these atoms becoming ionized as a result of the collisions.

To describe the absorption of gamma rays it is necessary to describe the energy of the radiation in terms of a photon or quantum of light energy, equal to hv, where h is Planck's constant and v is the vibration frequency of the radiation. That is, the wave is taken to consist of discrete 'parcels' of energy, the photons. These can interact with the atoms of an absorber in the following ways.

(a) *The Compton effect*—If a photon collides with an orbital electron (Chapter 7) there is an interchange of energy. The electron is driven out of its orbit and the photon is deflected with altered energy. This is known as the Compton effect. The loss of energy of the photon is given by the sum of the increased kinetic energy of the orbital electron and its 'binding energy'. Thus, in the absorber, a gamma ray may be deflected with a decreased vibration frequency, i.e. an increased wavelength (*Figure 4.1*).

Provided that the absorber is sufficiently thick, then by a succession of collisions, the gamma ray finally loses almost all of its energy, producing in the absorber a number of 'secondary electrons' which themselves eventually become absorbed by a process similar to that for beta particles. A gamma ray entering an absorber of limited size may be scattered out of the absorber after one or more Compton processes, emerging with a longer wavelength (lower energy). This implies that an initially mono-energetic beam of gamma rays entering a moderately thick absorber will emerge with a continuous range of energies. This process is called 'degradation' and is important in the calculation of the minimum thickness required for

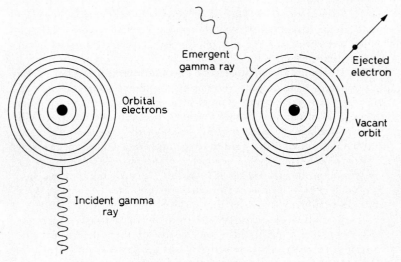

Figure 4.1. The Compton effect

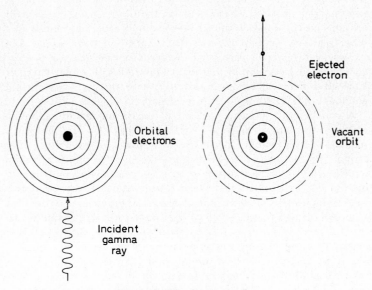

Figure 4.2. The photoelectric effect

radiation shields for nuclear reactors and other intense sources of gamma radiation.

(b) *Photoelectric effect*—The second process by which gamma radiation can be absorbed is the 'photoelectric effect' (*Figure 4.2*), in which the entire energy of a photon is converted into that of an electron emitted from the outer orbit.

The Compton and photoelectric effects are rival processes for the loss of energy from gamma photons during their passage through an absorber. In general, the photoelectric effect is the more probable in the case of gamma rays of lower energy and absorbers of high atomic number. A third process is that of the disappearance of a gamma photon with the simultaneous appearance of a negative and a positive electron ('*pair production*'). This process corresponds to conversion of the gamma ray into matter, as predicted by Einstein's Special Theory of Relativity, and becomes important only at gamma energies significantly greater than 1 MeV.

The formation of secondary electrons by the passage of gamma rays through matter provides the means for their detection. For example, a Geiger tube is sensitive to any gamma ray photon which undergoes a Compton or photoelectric collision with an atom of the gas or an atom of the material of the walls of the tube. Since the gamma rays are very penetrating and the Geiger counter normally contains only gas at a reduced pressure in a relatively thin-walled tube, very few gamma photons are trapped in these ways. The intrinsic efficiency of a normal Geiger tube for gamma photons is only about 1 per cent of that for beta particles of similar energies. This efficiency can be improved by lining the tube (except the window) with lead foil, to trap more gamma photons.

A much more efficient method of measuring gamma photons is that of trapping them in a transparent block of a suitable crystal such as sodium iodide (activated with traces of thallium). The crystal has two functions. First, it traps most of the gamma photons which strike it, with a degree of efficiency which depends on the photon energy and on the size of the crystal. A type of crystal sometimes used in modern radiochemical laboratories is in the form of a cylinder of diameter 2 in. and height 2 in. The sample for measurement is inserted into a vertical well of $\frac{1}{2}$ in. diameter which extends to the centre of the cylinder. With this arrangement, about 50 per cent of the gamma photons of energy 1 MeV, and 70 per cent of those of energy 0·5 MeV, produce secondary electrons inside the crystal. Because the crystal contains iodine atoms, of moderately high atomic number, the photoelectric process is appreciable and below 0·3 MeV it predominates. Again, the crystal is sufficiently large for those gamma photons which experience energy loss by the Compton effect to have a high probability of a subsequent complete capture by the photoelectric effect (or by a succession of Compton processes) before they escape from the crystal. For these two reasons, most of the gamma photons which undergo *any* energy loss in the crystal do in fact lose *all* their energy. The second function of the sodium iodide crystal is that of a phosphor— a solid which can transform the kinetic energy of a secondary electron into a flash of light energy. The traces of thallium impurity, deliberately introduced during manufacture, are said to 'activate' the sodium iodide crystal lattice to produce the properties of a phosphor (in a similar way the zinc sulphide used in the alpha scintillation counter is activated by traces of silver as an impurity).

The secondary electron, arising, say from the photoelectric capture of a 1 MeV gamma photon by an iodine atom in the crystal, almost instantaneously produces several thousand quanta of visible light, at a fixed wavelength which is characteristic of the particular phosphor, and which for sodium iodide activated by thallium has a maximum at 4100 Å (corresponding to a quantum of about 3 eV). The light can be reflected from the walls of the crystal if it is surrounded by zinc oxide powder inside an outer metal can, and most of the light quanta can be made to leave the crystal at its bottom face, which is arranged to be in good optical contact with the window of a photomultiplier tube (*Figure 4.3*). This device re-converts the light quanta to photoelectrons at a cathode made of an alkali metal such as caesium. About 10 photoelectrons are obtained per hundred quanta. The photomultiplier tube then functions as an electron multiplier to amplify the photoelectric 'pulse' by a factor of 10^6 or more. Each gamma photon which produces one (or more) secondary electrons in the crystal releases an amplified pulse from the photomultiplier tube. These pulses can be further amplified and counted in a scaling circuit like the pulses from a Geiger tube. Compared with the Geiger tube, the combination of sodium iodide crystal and photomultiplier tube has two great advantages as a detector of gamma radiation, especially for weak sources:

(*a*) The intrinsic efficiency is much higher;

(*b*) Unlike the discharge pulses from a Geiger tube, the pulses from the photomultiplier are not all of similar magnitude, but are proportional to the energy which was released by the gamma photon during its interaction with the crystal.

This means that it is possible to discriminate between gamma photons of different energies, by the use of electronic 'pulse analysers' as described for alpha spectrometry on p. 16. Although 'pulse analysers' are very expensive instruments, especially those which 'sort' the pulses simultaneously into 100 different channels according to their exact magnitude, they are becoming widely used in radio-chemical laboratories because they permit the rapid identification of the radioactive element in an unknown sample, even when the

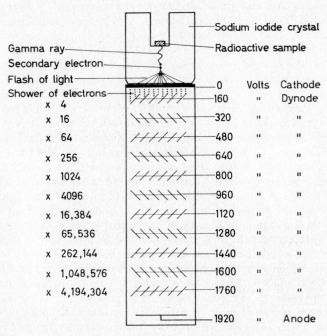

Figure 4.3. Scintillation counter for gamma rays

total amount of radioactivity is very small. The method of 'gamma scintillation spectrometry' has been used, for example in exact studies of the nature and quantity of radioactive 'fall-out' in the atmosphere and stratosphere, arising from the explosion of nuclear weapons. *Figure 4.4* illustrates the quantitative analysis of the gamma radiations which had been collected on vegetation exposed to 'fall-out' near a nuclear explosion. Gamma energies of 0·14, 0·36, 0·50, 0·76 and 1·6 MeV can be recognized, due to the fission products cerium-141 and -143; iodine-131; ruthenium-103 and -106; zirconium-95 and niobium-95; and barium-140 and lanthanum-140 respectively.

It may be noted that the peaks in the gamma scintillation spectrum are much broader (when expressed as a percentage of the mean energy) than those in an alpha pulse spectrum (*Figure 2.7*) obtained with an ionization chamber. The gamma photons are

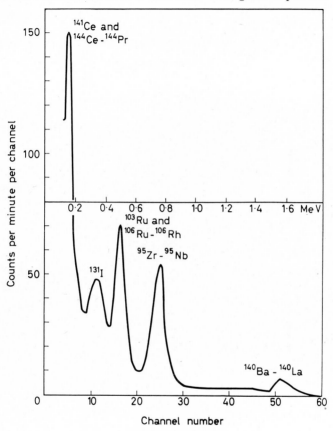

Figure 4.4. Gamma scintillation spectrometry

themselves mono-energetic, like the alpha particles, but a statistical distribution of energy about a mean value appears as a result of the detailed mechanisms of the sequence of processes: gamma photon → secondary electron → shower of light quanta → shower of electrons at photocathode → amplified pulse. A further distortion in the pulse spectrum (*Figure 4.5*) is caused by some gamma photons transferring only part of their energy to a secondary electron, by the Compton process. This in fact gives rise to a range of pulse heights, all of them

4

less than the full pulse height corresponding to a photoelectric capture in the sodium iodide. These subsidiary pulses can be reduced by the use of larger crystals, up to 6 in. in diameter and height, with correspondingly large photo-multipliers. In a sufficiently large

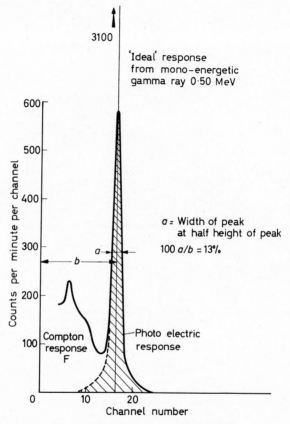

Figure 4.5. Gamma spectrum (0·50 MeV)

crystal, all the energy of gamma photons must be transferred either by a single photoelectric process or by a succession of Compton processes followed by a photoelectric process. The time scale of either process is so rapid (of the order of a few millionths of a second) that the photomultiplier cannot distinguish between them, and the full pulse height is recorded.

The use of large scintillation counters, with their high efficiency of detection, is very suitable for the quantitative analysis of relatively

42

weak sources of gamma radiation. The accuracy of the determination of the *energies* of the individual gamma rays is limited by the broadness of the peaks. Highly accurate determinations of energy can be made by crystal diffraction (p. 34) or indirectly by magnetic spectrometry (p. 31) of the secondary electrons which are released when the gamma rays are allowed to bombard a metal target. The results of such work are illustrated by the radioactive fission product, iodine-131, which is found to have *five* distinct gamma rays, of energies 0·08, 0·284, 0·364, 0·637 and 0·722 MeV. It is quite

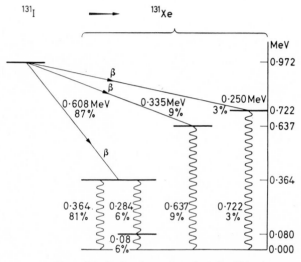

Figure 4.6. Nuclear decay scheme for iodine-131

common for several energies to be present in this manner. Mostly, these gamma rays accompany beta particles (as for iodine-131) or alpha particles (as for radium). The accurate study of the energies and relative abundance of all the radiations emitted from a single radioactive body, such as iodine-131, makes it possible to draw an energy diagram, known as a 'decay scheme' (*Figure 4.6.*) Special experimental methods (coincidence counting) are used to correlate particular energies of beta (or alpha) particles with particular energies of gamma rays. The right-hand column of the decay scheme represents the product of radioactive decay, which in this case is the stable isotope, xenon-131. The emission of a beta (or alpha) particle from a radioactive body often leaves the product (as in this case) in what is called an 'excited state', i.e. containing surplus energy. This energy may be released by the emission of gamma rays. Diagrams such as *Figure 4.6* are based upon purely experimental measurements, but are of great importance in the development of theories of nuclear structure, for they give an insight into the excited energy levels inside the nucleus.

It may be noted that the ratio of beta particles to disintegrations is exactly unity. The total number of gamma photons per disintegration is not usually unity, as it depends upon the complexities of the decay scheme. Some beta emitters reach the ground state of the product directly, without the need to radiate the surplus energy as gamma rays—an example is:

$$^{90}\text{Sr} \rightarrow {}^{90}\text{Y} + \beta$$

(0·61 MeV, no gamma radiation.)

Sometimes the ratio of gamma to beta is as high as 2/1:

$$^{60}\text{Co} \rightarrow {}^{60}\text{Ni} + \beta$$

(0·31 MeV, followed by two successive gamma rays, the first of 1·33 MeV and the second of 1·17 MeV).

The practical problem sometimes arises in radioactive analysis—what is the effective ratio of 'unconverted' gamma rays to total 'beta particles plus conversion electrons' from a particular radioactive isotope? This could arise, for example, if one wished to correlate measurements made on a sample of iodine-131 (*a*) with a Geiger counter (beta rays plus conversion electrons), (*b*) with a sodium iodide scintillation counter (unconverted gamma rays). In this case it is essential to look at the published decay scheme (e.g. D. Strominger, J. M. Hollander and G. T. Seaborg 'Table of Isotopes' in *Reviews of Modern Physics*, Vol. 30, April 1958, pp. 584–904) together with the list of 'conversion coefficients' for the gamma rays. It must be explained that the abundances cited for the gamma rays in *Figure 4.6* take no account of any internal conversion which may occur once the gamma photon has left the nucleus (p. 33). These conversion coefficients, α, are defined as the abundance of the conversion electrons divided by the abundance of the residual unconverted gamma ray. The conversion electrons are mainly from the K shell (see Chapter 7), and the coefficient is often written as α_K. Values of α_K for the internal conversion of the gamma rays of iodine-131 are given in Table 4.1.

Table 4.1. Internal Conversion Coefficients for Iodine-131

Gamma energy (MeV)	0·08	0·284	0·364	0·637	0·722
α_K	1·7	0·05	0·02	0·004	0·003

The conversion coefficients are usually very small for gamma energies of 0·3 MeV or more; a noteworthy exception is the fission product caesium-137 (beta active, half-life 30 years). This is normally at equilibrium with a daughter product, the excited state of barium-137 (of independent half-life = 2·6 min) which decays to the stable state of barium-137 by the release of a single gamma ray of energy 0·66 MeV. This gamma ray, which is often used to measure caesium-137 in practical analyses, has $\alpha_K = 0·1$.

5

THE MATHEMATICS OF RADIOACTIVE DECAY

SIMPLE RADIOACTIVE DECAY

We will now study radioactive decay mathematically, using polonium, a natural radioactive species, as an example.

If one were to carry out monthly measurements of the alpha-radioactivity of a sample of polonium, the results would be similar to those shown in Table 5.1. The radioactivity is seen to decrease

Table 5.1. Measurements of the Radioactivity of Polonium-210 at Successive Monthly Intervals

Time (days)	α-Radioactivity (disint./min)	$\log_{10}$ (disint./min)
0	10,000	4·000
30	8,606	3·935
60	7,406	3·870
90	6,374	3·804
120	5,478	3·739
180	4,061	3·608
270	2,589	3·413
365	1,646	3·216

exponentially, as shown in *Figure 5.1*, the results fitting the equations:

$$-\frac{dN}{dt} = \lambda N \qquad \text{(The differential equation)} \qquad (5.1)$$

$$N = N_0 e^{-\lambda t} \quad \text{(The integrated form)} \qquad (5.2)$$

where N is the number of atoms of polonium present at any given time, t, and λ is a constant characteristic of the particular radioactive substance, the derivative $-dN/dt$ representing the rate of loss of atoms of polonium due to radioactive decay. These are the fundamental equations for the mathematical treatment of radioactive decay. Four important comments must be made on them.

(1) The equations are of the same mathematical type as those for chemical reactions of the first order. Strictly speaking, they

apply only to the behaviour of a very large number of atoms. The behaviour of any particular atom—whether it will decay or not during some specified interval of time—cannot be predicted. Statistically, what we can predict is the behaviour of a large number of atoms, sufficient for statistical fluctuations to be smoothed out.

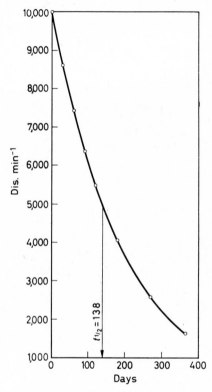

Figure 5.1. Decrease in radioactivity of polonium-210 with time

Even so, the fluctuations are easily noticed in laboratory measurements of radioactivity. If the alpha activity of polonium had been measured during ten successive 1 min intervals (the total time interval is very short compared with the half-life of 138 days, so that decay may be neglected), the results would be similar to those shown in Table 5.2. The spread of the results about the mean value follows a Poisson distribution (*Figure 5.2*).

In order to obtain an accurate value, one has to take the average of many measurements or (more conveniently) extend a single

Table 5.2. Measurements of the Radioactivity of Polonium-210
Made Over Successive Short Intervals of Time

	(counts/min)	Δ (*deviation from mean*)	Δ²
	5,782	+129	16,640
	5,714	+61	3,721
	5,657	+4	16
	5,612	−41	1,681
	5,691	+38	1,444
	5,500	−153	23,410
	5,707	+54	2,916
	5,597	−56	3,136
	5,619	−34	1,156
	5,647	−6	36
Mean	5,653		5,416
(*Mean*)$^{\frac{1}{2}}$	75·2		73·6

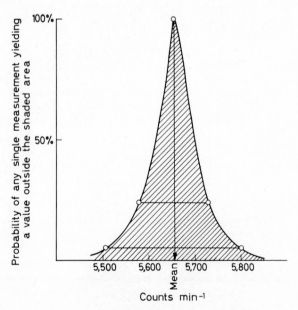

Figure 5.2. Statistical error curve (Poisson distribution)

48

measurement over a longer time interval. The scatter in the measurements is specified by the coefficient of variation (C.V.) which is given in Table 5.2 by:

$$\text{C.V.} = \frac{100\sigma}{\bar{A}} \text{ per cent}$$

where σ^2 is the mean value of Δ^2, and $\bar{A}$ is the mean value of A, the number of counts per interval.

From probability theory we would expect

$$\text{C.V.} = \frac{100}{\bar{A}^{\frac{1}{2}}} \text{ per cent}$$

This equation expresses the fact that in a Poisson distribution, the coefficient of variation is equal to the square root of the average value, expressed as a percentage. This is illustrated in Table 5.2 where the coefficient of variation for any individual count is experimentally:

$$\frac{73\cdot6}{5,653} \times 100 = 1\cdot30 \text{ per cent}$$

The expected coefficient of variation for a single count of 5,653 is theoretically:

$$\frac{100}{(5653)^{\frac{1}{2}}} = 1\cdot33 \text{ per cent}$$

in good agreement. Having calculated the coefficient of variation for a single measurement of the radioactivity we may estimate the reliability of the single measurement with the aid of the following rules of statistics.

On average,

2 measurements out of 3 lie within
$\pm$ C.V. of the mean

19 measurements out of 20 lie within
$\pm$ 2 C.V. of the mean

For the measurements recorded in Table 5.2, we would expect 2 out of 3 to fall in the range $5,653 \pm 1\cdot3$ per cent, i.e. $5,653 \pm 74$ or in the range 5,579 to 5,727 (*Figure 5.2*).

The range of error of the *mean* value is, of course, less than that of the single measurements. For the mean of 10 measurements,

$$\text{C.V.} = \frac{1\cdot3}{(10)^{\frac{1}{2}}} = 0\cdot4 \text{ per cent}$$

(2) The second equation may be changed into a logarithmic form:

$$\log_{10} N = \log_{10} N_0 - \frac{\lambda \cdot t}{2 \cdot 303}$$

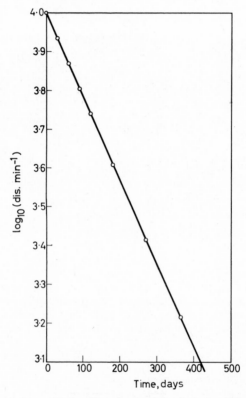

Figure 5.3. Decrease in logarithm of radioactivity of polonium-210 with time

whence from equation 5.1 we may derive that

$$\log_{10}\left(\frac{\mathrm{d}N}{\mathrm{d}t}\right) = \log_{10}\left(\frac{\mathrm{d}N_0}{\mathrm{d}t}\right) - \frac{\lambda \cdot t}{2 \cdot 303}$$

This form is very valuable for converting experimental results such as those in Table 5.1 into a convenient graphical form. Instead of plotting $\mathrm{d}N/\mathrm{d}t$ as a function of time (*Figure 5.1*) we plot $\log_{10}$ ($\mathrm{d}N/\mathrm{d}t$) as a linear function of time (*Figure 5.3*). It is even possible to avoid the labour of consulting tables of logarithms, by using semi-logarithmic paper (*Figure 5.4*).

(3) We have now to consider the concept of 'half-life' (*Figure 5.1*). This is defined as the time required for half of the radioactive atoms

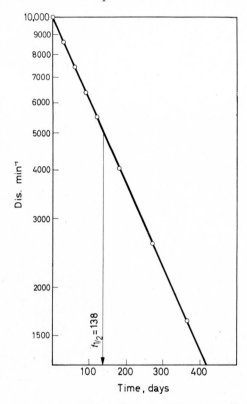

Figure 5.4. Decrease of radioactivity of polonium-210 with time (semi-log scale)

to decay, and is usually denoted by the symbol, $t_{\frac{1}{2}}$. It may easily be related to the fundamental equations: in equation 5.2, substitute $t_{\frac{1}{2}}$ for t, and $N_0/2$ for N. Then:

$$\frac{N_0}{2} = N_0 e^{-\lambda t_{\frac{1}{2}}}$$

or

$$\lambda t_{\frac{1}{2}} = \log_e 2 = 0 \cdot 693$$

or

$$t_{\frac{1}{2}} = \frac{0 \cdot 693}{\lambda} \qquad (5.3)$$

51

The half-life is best measured experimentally by plotting a series of measurements, as recorded in Table 5.1, on semi-logarithmic graph paper (*Figure 5.4*). The half-life may then be read off the time axis at the point corresponding to 50 per cent decay. It sometimes happens that the points do not lie on a straight line (*Figure 5.5*)

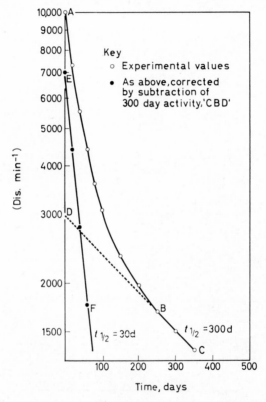

Figure 5.5. Decrease in radioactivity of a mixture of radioactive species with time (semi-log scale)

and this is a valuable indication that more than one radioactive species was present in the sample. It is then possible by graphical analysis to resolve the mixed decay equations, at least in favourable cases. The activity of longest half-life is recognized from the linear region of the graph, *BC*, which is extrapolated back to *D*. The values in the region *AB* are now corrected by subtracting the values taken from *DB*. The corrected values are re-plotted on the graph (*EF*).

(4) The equations 5.1 and 5.2, being fundamental to radio-

active decay, apply even to sources such as uranium, thorium or radium which suffer no measurable decay during normal experiments, i.e. their half-lives appear to be infinite. This is only to say that their half-lives are very large in comparison with the periods of days or perhaps of weeks which we can afford to allocate to the experiments. Nevertheless, these half-lives can still be accurately calculated from a knowledge of the terms $-\dfrac{dN}{dt}$ and N in equation 5.1. Rearranging the equation, after substituting $\dfrac{0 \cdot 693}{t_{\frac{1}{2}}}$ for λ (equation 5.3), we arrive at a modified equation:

$$t_{\frac{1}{2}} = 0 \cdot 693 \bigg/ \left(-\frac{1}{N} \cdot \frac{dN}{dt}\right) \tag{5.4}$$

The term $-\dfrac{1}{N} \cdot \dfrac{dN}{dt}$ represents the so-called 'specific activity' of the particular radioactive species, i.e. the disintegration rate divided by the original number of atoms. Because the half-life is large, the value of N does not change appreciably during the measurements. A worked example will serve to show this method of calculating the half-life.

A radioactive source which contains exactly 10^{-8} g of freshly purified radium is found to give an alpha count of 10,900 counts/min when measured in an ionization counter of geometrical efficiency, 50 per cent. Thus $-\dfrac{dN}{dt}$, corrected for geometrical efficiency of the alpha counter $= 10{,}900/0 \cdot 5 = 21{,}800$ atoms/min.

$N =$ the number of radium atoms in 10^{-8} g, which we have to calculate from a knowledge of the atomic weight of radium (226) and of Avogadro's number ($6 \cdot 02 \times 10^{23}$, being the number of atoms of any element which make up the atomic weight in g).

$$N = 6 \cdot 02 \times 10^{23} \times \frac{10^{-8}}{226} = 2 \cdot 66 \times 10^{13} \text{ atoms}$$

Substituting the above values of $-\dfrac{dN}{dt}$ and of N in equation 5.4,

$$t_{\frac{1}{2}} = 0 \cdot 693 \bigg/ \left(\frac{2 \cdot 18 \times 10^{4}}{2 \cdot 66 \times 10^{13}}\right) \text{ min}$$

$$= 0 \cdot 693 \times \frac{2 \cdot 66}{2 \cdot 18} \times 10^{9} \text{ min} = 0 \cdot 845 \times 10^{9} \text{ min}$$

$$= 1{,}610 \text{ years}$$

Even longer half-lives may be measured for uranium ($4\cdot5 \times 10^9$ years) and thorium ($1\cdot4 \times 10^{10}$ years), derived from experimental measurements of their specific activities. The specific activity of radium, measured accurately, is $3\cdot70 \times 10^{10}$ disintegrations sec^{-1} g^{-1}, and this figure is called a 'curie' and is often used as a standard in expressing disintegration rates, e.g., p. 151.

RADIOACTIVE DECAY SERIES

The four sections above represent useful developments from the fundamental equations, which relate to the radioactive decay of a single species such as polonium-210. In order to make quantitative calculations about the behaviour of more complicated systems, such as the decay series which starts with thorium and ends with the active deposits (Chapter 6), we have to set up more elaborate differential equations. The principle is quite straightforward—for any member of the series, say thorium X, we express $\dfrac{\mathrm{d}N}{\mathrm{d}t}$ as the algebraic sum of two factors; $\lambda_1 N'$, the rate of radioactive decay of the preceding member of the chain; $\lambda_2 N$, the rate of radioactive decay of thorium X itself, thus

$$\frac{\mathrm{d}N}{\mathrm{d}t} = \lambda_1 N' - \lambda_2 N \tag{5.5}$$

If the preceding member is comparatively long-lived, e.g. thorium or uranium, the expression $\lambda_1 N'$ is essentially a constant, A.

Then $$\frac{\mathrm{d}N}{\mathrm{d}t} = A - \lambda_2 N$$

or $$N = \frac{A}{\lambda_2} (1 - \mathrm{e}^{\lambda_2 \cdot t}) \tag{5.6}$$

The rate of radioactive decay of thorium X after a time $t = \lambda_2 \cdot N$, where $\lambda_2 \cdot N = A(1 - \mathrm{e}^{-\lambda_2 \cdot t})$. This equation is used to calculate the 'growth curve' C in *Figure 6.2*, with a modification to allow for the constant activity due to the long-lived thorium parent. (It is common in a case such as we have been discussing to speak of the first member of the decay chain as the 'parent' and the following members as 'daughters'.) It is interesting to note that in the particular example we have followed, where the half-life of the parent is very large compared with that of the daughter, the growth of the radioactivity of the daughter is governed by its own half-life—a very short-lived daughter rapidly grows into equilibrium with its parent. This situation is quite common in practical radio-chemistry, e.g. uranium X, daughter of uranium-238; yttrium-90, daughter of the fission product strontium-90, but it sometimes confuses the beginner to the subject, who expects the daughter 'to have to wait for the parent to decay'—implying that it must wait a very long time.

The fallacy in this line of thought is worth pursuing further. Obviously the parent will not have decayed very much over a short time in terms of actual numbers of atoms, therefore there will not be many atoms of the daughter present. But because of its short half-life, these relatively few atoms can produce a substantial radioactivity. It may, in fact, be shown that when a decay chain is fully in dynamic equilibrium,

$$\lambda_1 N_1 = \lambda_2 N_2 = \lambda_3 N_3 = \lambda_4 N_4 \text{ - - - } = \lambda_n N_n$$

where λ_1, λ_2 - - - λ_n are inversely proportional to the corresponding half-lives. It follows that each member of the chain will contribute the same decay rate—in a four-membered chain, each member being alpha active, the total alpha activity at equilibrium is four times that of the parent member. It also follows that the total numbers of atoms (or less exactly, the actual weights) of any member of the decay chain is proportional to the particular half-life. To take a specific case, the weight of thorium X ($t_\frac{1}{2} = 3\cdot6$ days) in equilibrium with 1 g of the parent element, thorium ($t_\frac{1}{2} = 1\cdot4 \times 10^{10}$ years) may be calculated.

$$\text{Weight of thorium X} = \frac{t_\frac{1}{2}(\text{Th X})}{t_\frac{1}{2}(\text{Th})} \cdot \frac{\text{At. Wt. (Th X)}}{\text{At. Wt. (Th)}}$$

$$= \frac{3\cdot6}{1\cdot4 \times 10^{10} \times 365} \cdot \frac{224}{232}$$

$$= 6\cdot8 \times 10^{-13} \text{ g}$$

The mathematical treatment of neutron activation is given in Chapter 8.

6

CHEMICAL ASPECTS OF RADIOACTIVE CHANGE

Much of the material in the first four chapters of this book has been concerned with purely physical measurements and discoveries—measurements of the mass and velocity of particles; discoveries in electricity, magnetism and electromagnetic radiation. In schools and universities, physics and chemistry are still treated as entirely separate subjects, while in the research field the boundaries are becoming less and less distinct. The merging of the two sciences is shown by the early work of Marie Curie in her search for a new element in pitchblende (Chapter 1). She combined the chemical technique of qualitative analysis with the physical measurement of radioactivity in an ionization chamber. Chemistry again appeared in the identification of the alpha particle as an atom of helium carrying two positive charges: thus the transmutation of one chemical element into another—for centuries the dream of alchemists—was now an accomplished fact.

These are by no means the only samples of the role of chemistry in the study of radioactivity; indeed a study of the transmutation of radium (at. wt. 226) to helium (at. wt. 4) suggests that it is probably accompanied by the production of some third element, of atomic weight intermediate between 4 and 226, possibly $= 226-4n$, where n is an integer. The investigation of such chemical products of radioactive change forms the branch of chemistry known as radiochemistry.

Some of the earliest work in radiochemistry, following the pioneer discovery of polonium and radium by the Curies, was prompted by the observation that certain radioactive materials appeared to emit a radioactive 'emanation' which in turn produced a secondary source of radioactivity (the 'excited activity'), on the surface of neighbouring objects. The 'excited activity' remained when the original source was removed: it was confined to the surface of the object and could be removed by mechanical abrasion or by the action of acids. The strength of 'emanation' from a given sample of thorium appeared to depend on its previous physical and chemical treatment. It was also difficult to reproduce exactly the amount of the 'excited activity' and the distance over which it spread.

Rutherford and Soddy looked more closely into these puzzling observations, using the apparatus shown diagrammatically in *Figure 6.1*, in which a stream of air or other gas is blown over some powdered crystals of a thorium salt and then over various chemical reagents before being examined for alpha activity in an ionization chamber. It was found that the amount of alpha activity due to 'emanation', detected in the chamber using a given sample of thorium, depended

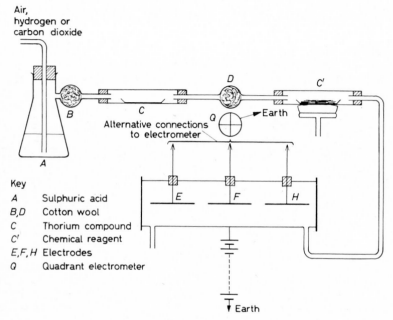

Figure 6.1. Apparatus for studying the emanation from thorium

only on the rate of air flow, being unaffected by the chemical reagents. However, the emanation did *not* appear in the ionization chamber if the intermediate vessel was immersed in liquid air. These observations caused Rutherford and Soddy to postulate that the emanation was a gas (thorium emanation or 'thoron'). Because the gas was not affected by passing it over heated platinum black, palladium black, zinc dust, lead chromate or magnesium powder, nor by passing it through dilute or concentrated sulphuric acid, it was supposed to be one of the series of inert gases, of which helium, neon, argon, krypton and xenon had recently been discovered by Sir William Ramsay and others. Immediately the supply of fresh gas is cut off, the alpha radioactivity of the gas drops to one-half of its value in each 52 sec. Thus the thorium emanation is under-going radioactive decay and has a half-life of 52 sec.

Despite its instability, it was possible to study the effect of chemical reagents by constantly sweeping the emanation out of the thorium source by a steady flow of air, hydrogen or carbon dioxide. This implies that 'new' gas is liberated from the original source as fast as 'old' gas is lost; that is, we have a system which is in dynamic equilibrium.

If the ionization chamber is isolated, then after several half-lives have elapsed, practically all the thorium emanation which has been blown out of the thorium salt will have disappeared, but during this process the 'excited activity' is formed on the walls of the vessel, and this is itself radioactive, with a half-life of 11 h.

A rather similar chain of radioactive processes can be traced, starting with the element radium. In this case the 'radium emana-tion' (or radon) has a half-life of 3·8 days. Like thoron, it leaves an 'excited activity.'

Chemical studies on solutions of thorium salts by Soddy and Rutherford, revealed that a large fraction of the alpha activity of the original thorium remained in the filtrate following the pre-cipitation of thorium hydroxide with ammonia, and this separation was only effective when *ammonia* was used to precipitate the thorium —it did not work when phosphate, oxalate or carbonate were used as reagents. Furthermore, when the filtrate was treated with a stream of air it gave an emanation just like the original salt of thorium. These observations suggested that the thorium contained traces of some other radioactive element, which Rutherford and Soddy called thorium X, which was itself the direct source of the emanation.

It may be seen that the thorium X is not a completely indepen-dent substance present as a stray impurity in the thorium, for it is linked with the thorium in a dynamic equilibrium. This is most easily understood if we study the change with time of the total alpha activity of three different samples. Sample A is a thorium salt. Sample B contains thorium X, freshly prepared from a solution of this thorium salt by evaporation of the filtrate after precipitating the thorium with ammonia and filtering off the thorium hydroxide. Sample C is the dried thorium hydroxide prepared from this same solution. The alpha activities of each of the three sources as a function of time are shown in *Figure 6.2* (the experimental results have been corrected for the varying degree of absorption of alpha particles in the crystals or powders, also for the varying degree of retention of the gaseous emanation by occlusion in these solids).

The alpha activity of the untreated thorium (A) remains constant over the period of measurement. The freshly separated thorium X (B) carries with it three-quarters of this activity, leaving one-quarter with the 'stripped' thorium (C). The activity of the thorium X falls exponentially with a half-life of 3·6 days. Surprisingly, the activity of the stripped thorium actually increases, until after a fortnight it is back at full strength. At any intermediate time, say d days, the sum of the activities of sources B and C makes up the full extent of

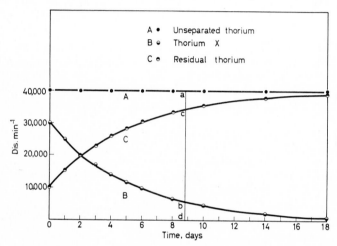

Figure 6.2. Changes in alpha activity with time, with fractions isolated from thorium series

the activity in the untreated thorium (A). In *Figure 6.2*, $bd + cd = ad$, wherever we choose to place d along the 'time' axis.

These results imply that thorium X is present in a state of dynamic equilibrium with the thorium, just as we have already concluded that the thorium emanation was in dynamic equilibrium with thorium. The overall sequence may be represented as:

$$\text{Th} \xrightarrow{\alpha} \text{Th X} \xrightarrow{\alpha} \text{Th emanation} \xrightarrow{\alpha} \text{Excited activity} \xrightarrow{\alpha} ?$$

the last stage being unresolved. The sequence is purely diagrammatic, since it is possible that other intermediates are present. One intermediate was later found between thorium and thorium X (see *Figure 6.4*).

A physical analogy (first used by Soddy) is that of water flowing along a series of reservoirs of decreasing capacity—say a series of beakers connected by small outlet tubes near their bases (*Figure 6.3*).

When the system has reached a steady state, water flows through the series of beakers without any change in the water level in the individual beakers. If the smallest beaker is removed and replaced by an empty beaker, there are now two separate systems. The smallest beaker discharges itself, while the replacement beaker fills until dynamic equilibrium is restored.

About 1902, Rutherford and Soddy recognized that the dynamic

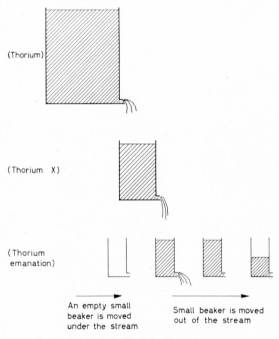

(Thorium)

(Thorium X)

(Thorium emanation)

An empty small beaker is moved under the stream

Small beaker is moved out of the stream

Figure 6.3. The hydraulic analogy

equilibrium in the thorium, thorium X, thorium emanation series, indicated that radioactivity involved the disintegration of atoms and the transmutation of one element into another. Later investigations filled in many of the details, and the reaction of thorium radioactivity can now be expressed as:

Th (at. wt. 232) $\rightarrow$ 2He (at. wt. 4) + Th X (at. wt. 224)

$\downarrow$

He + Th emanation (at. wt. 220)

The mathematics of radioactive decay, discussed in Chapter 5, show that the actual number of atoms of a daughter element such as thorium X is in inverse proportion to its half-life.

It may easily be realized that many radioactive species, like thorium X ($t_{\frac{1}{2}}$ = 3·6 days), are normally present in our experiments in quite unweighable amounts, and are far below the level of normal chemical methods of detection. A calculation on p. 55 shows that 1 g of thorium-232 will be in equilibrium with 7×10^{-13} g of thorium X. We can study the chemical properties of these minute traces only by processes such as ion-exchange, chromatography, and solvent extraction, which in general work as well with a few atoms as with many, or by the process of co-precipitation with a suitable carrier. This latter process is essentially the one which was used by Marie Curie in her radiochemical experiments with pitchblende. Only the merest traces of polonium and of radium were present in her early experiments before she extended the chemical separations almost to a factory scale. Yet those few atoms of the new radioactive elements were correctly sorted into their correct qualitative analysis groups, riding upon the backs, as it were, of certain common non-radioactive elements which happened to be present as impurities in the pitchblende, e.g. bismuth in the qualitative analysis Group 2 and barium in Group 5. The weight of radium present in some of the solutions used by Marie Curie was far less than 10^{-6} g, and this is below the solubility product of radium carbonate under the conditions for the precipitation of Group 5. Nevertheless the radium is almost completely co-precipitated with barium carbonate. Not every precipitate has this same effect, for scarcely any of the radium would accompany a precipitate of ferric hydroxide under Group 3 conditions, or of bismuth sulphide under Group 2 conditions. Generally speaking, a reagent and conditions which would lead to the true precipitation of *visible* amounts of radium if they had been present, will also lead to the *co-precipitation* of *trace* quantities of radium upon a suitable carrier. Since the solubility products of radium salts are similar to those of barium, which is a member of the same vertical sub-group of the Periodic Table, any precipitate of a barium salt will serve to 'carry' traces of radium (nevertheless, the chemistry of these two elements is not identical—a fact which will be taken up later in this book—see Chapter 9, on the discovery of nuclear fission).

It was, of course, fortunate that the pitchblende which was analysed by Marie Curie contained sufficient impurities such as lead, bismuth, copper, iron and barium to give visible precipitates under each of the qualitative analysis groups:

Group I,   dilute hydrochloric acid,   e.g. Lead
Group II,   as above, with hydrogen sulphide,   e.g. Bismuth
Group III, dilute ammonium chloride and ammonia, e.g. Iron
Group IV,   as above, with ammonium sulphide,   e.g. Copper
Group V,   dilute ammonium carbonate,   e.g. Barium

The *absence* of alpha activity upon the precipitates from Groups I and IV, just as much as the *presence* of alpha activity upon the precipitates from Groups II and V, gave the necessary chemical clues which were to lead to the discovery of polonium and of radium respectively.

This technique of radiochemical analysis has continued to be extremely important down to the present day. There was considerable work of this kind during the decade following the atomic disintegration theory of Rutherford and Soddy (1903–13). This theory, which postulated that radioactivity is a consequence of atomic disintegration, the atom expelling charged particles as rays and changing into a somewhat lighter atom of a different element, made it natural for radiochemists such as Soddy, Marckwald, Fleck, Russell, von Hevesey and Fajans to try to identify the successive radioactive elements in the stepwise disintegration paths of uranium, thorium, radium and actinium, including for example the 'active deposits' from thorium and radium emanations.

The investigation of the chemical nature of the 'active deposits' used an interesting combination of physical and chemical techniques. Several radioactive elements were found to be present, of half-lives in the region of minutes, days or weeks, i.e. a range of values that could quite conveniently be measured directly by successive tests on a given sample. The results can be interpreted mathematically and graphically (*Figure 5.5*), so as to reveal the component half-lives of the individual constituents of the mixture—provided that the mixture is not too complex. Fortunately, a chemical 'sorting out' of the active deposits can also be carried out by qualitative analysis.

The active deposits from thoron and radon may be dissolved in acids and then small quantities of the salts of various non-radioactive metals may be added to the solution. These metals are added as inactive carriers—like the metallic impurities present in pitchblende. The chosen metals would include a representative of each of the five main groups in the qualitative analysis tables, say silver, bismuth, iron, zinc and barium.

By a combination of the techniques of the graphical analysis of decay curves and of the chemical analysis into groups, it slowly became possible to identify the constituents of the active deposits.

No new elements were detected, but two known elements were shown to be present in radioactive forms—so-called radio-lead and radio-bismuth. Similar radiochemical analysis of solutions of thorium, of uranium and of radium again revealed radioactive forms of commonly known elements, including lead, bismuth, and thallium. The picture was complicated by the fact that more than one radioactive form of the same element could be detected. For example, a material called mesothorium was isolated by O. Hahn at Berlin in 1906 from a solution of thorium. Chemically it behaves exactly like radium; for example, both can be isolated on a barium carrier. Although it *is* possible, by refined chemical methods such as fractional precipitation, to separate radium from the carrier element barium, it is not possible so to separate a mixture of radium and mesothorium. Yet the two materials have different radioactive properties: their half-lives are respectively 1,620 years and 6·7 years.

Many new radioactive species were discovered before 1914 varying greatly in their half-lives and in the nature (alpha, beta or gamma) and energies of their radiations. The radioactive decay series starting with thorium and uranium as parents are now known to contain no fewer than 27 distinct radioactive species. The radiochemical techniques described above made it possible to classify these species according to their resemblance to known chemical elements, i.e. to assign a place to them in the Periodic Table of the Elements (*Figure 7.3*). Remarkably, it was found that the 27 species can all be assigned using only 10 places in the Periodic Table. The surprising fact is not that the radioactive substances are *new* elements, but that in so many cases they are chemically indistinguishable from certain *known* elements, of atomic number 81–92, some of which (Bi, Pb, Tl) were previously only known in a stable non-radioactive form. We have now to consider in detail the far-reaching implications of this chemical generalization. Between 1911 and 1913, Soddy (who was now at Glasgow University) made two very important contributions to the interpretation of these facts—firstly the recognition of isotopes and secondly the Displacement Laws of radioactive change.

(*a*) *Isotopes*—Only 10 places in the Periodic Table were sufficient to account for the chemical properties of 27 radioactive species, therefore some places would have to be occupied by more than one species (*Figure 6.4*). Mesothorium and radium can be separated from barium by chemical processes, e.g. fractional crystallization of the chlorides. It is not possible, however, to separate them from one another by normal chemical methods. Yet they are two separate identities with quite distinct radioactive properties. A basic principle of the Periodic Table is normally that each place corresponds to a single chemical element, with the one exception of the so-called 'rare earths', a group of 14 elements (lanthanum, etc.) of atomic numbers 57–71 which together occupy a single place, having very similar (but not strictly identical) chemical properties. Even the rare earths can be at least partially separated by the fractional crystallization of their salts, and they have in recent years been completely separated by the use of columns of ion

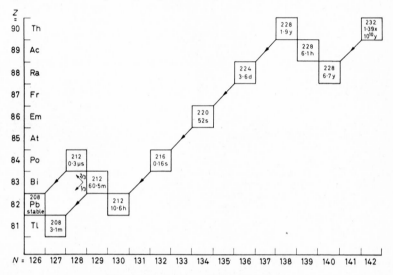

Figure 6.4. Thorium radioactive decay series

exchange resins. Not even this chemical technique will appreciably separate mesothorium from radium.

Other examples of two or more species which cannot be chemically separated, but which have differing radioactive properties, were also listed by Soddy, e.g. 'radio-thorium', 'ionium' and 'normal' thorium; radio-lead and 'normal' lead. Soddy coined the name 'Isotope' (Greek: isos topos, 'same place') for forms of the same chemical element which differed only in their physical properties (e.g. atomic weight, radioactivity). Since this recognition of 'isotopes' in 1913, it has been recognized that every chemical element can have several isotopes, most of which are radioactive.

Confirmation of Soddy's hypothesis came from research in 1919 by Aston, who was following up earlier work of Thomson (1912) on the positive rays formed by neon. Essentially the positive rays are fast-moving positively charged atoms. They are deflected by a magnetic field and by an electric field in such a way that all the rays with the same ratio of charge/mass (whatever their velocities) are focused on to one point of a photographic plate. This equipment of Aston's is usually called a 'mass spectrograph' (*Figure 6.5*) because it produces a dispersion spectrum according to mass, just as an 'optical spectrograph' produces a dispersion spectrum according to wavelength. The results showed that the pure chemical element, neon, was a mixture of two forms of atomic weights 20 and 22, in the ratio of 9:1 respectively. The 'average' atomic weight (strictly, the

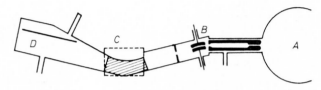

A   Vacuum tube containing
    traces of neon

B   Electric field

C   Magnetic field

D   Photographic plate

Figure 6.5. Aston's improved mass spectrograph
(From Tolansky *Radioactive Elements:* Longmans Green, London)

'weighted mean') becomes 20·2, which is the atomic weight normally ascribed to the element neon. Aston was able to show that most of the chemical elements were mixtures of isotopes which differed only in atomic weight.

Although Aston worked with elements which were not radioactive, his discovery suggested that pairs such as mesothorium and radium, may be isotopes differing only in atomic weight. This hypothesis is justified because of its success in helping to map out the Radioactive Decay Series in terms of the Periodic Table, as we shall see in the following section.

(*b*) *The Displacement Laws*—We have already referred to radiochemical investigations (p. 63) which reveal that the radioactivity of an element like uranium or thorium is accompanied by a transmutation from one chemical element to another and that a series of successive transmutations take place, until eventually the process terminates in a stable isotope of *lead*. In the course of these sequences, alpha, beta and gamma rays are emitted. In order to reduce the complex experimental observations to a coherent pattern, one might ask how the chemical result of any single stage is related to the type of radiation which is emitted. Soddy formulated a successful generalization in terms of the Periodic Table. His Displacement Laws stated that:

(*a*) the chemical result of the emission of an alpha particle is a transmutation to an element which is two places to the left in the Periodic Table;

(*b*) the chemical result of the emission of a beta particle is a transmutation to an element which is one place to the right in the Periodic Table;

(*c*) no chemical transmutation follows as a result of the emission of a gamma ray.

The application of these Laws may be illustrated with reference to the thorium decay series (*Figure 6.4*). The parent element, thorium, atomic weight 232·0, is one of those few elements which have only one main isotope, i.e. this is the only isotope which is important in affecting the atomic weight as measured chemically. The approximate atomic weights of the succeeding members of the series have been calculated by subtracting 4 units for each alpha particle. The various isotopes are plotted on a grid such that the vertical axis represents the atomic number and the horizontal axis represents the number of neutrons in the nucleus (this is obtained by subtracting the atomic number from the nearest whole number atomic weight).

Soddy's Displacement Laws are empirical generalizations which reduce a body of radiochemical facts to a tidy pattern—they do not directly tell us anything about the events within the atom which are responsible for these transmutations. However, they were one of three different lines of research which, about 1913, seemed to converge in finding a satisfactory explanation in terms of the nuclear theory of the atom, which is dealt with in the following chapter.

7

ATOMIC AND NUCLEAR STRUCTURE

J. Dalton's atomic theory (1805) had postulated that the atom, as the smallest unit of matter, was indivisible, and that elements differed only in the mass of their atoms: for most purposes, atoms could be imagined as hard spheres obeying the laws of Newtonian mechanics. Chemical combination of elements could be pictured as the combination of two or more atoms to form a 'compound atom' and the empirical concept of valency was introduced. The first discoveries which made inevitable some degree of concern with the structure of the atom were electrolysis, leading to Faraday's ionic theory, and isomerism in organic chemistry, which led to the recognition of directional valency. The ionic theory was interpreted by Stoney (1891) in terms of the loss and gain of charged particles, which he called electrons—thus, in a sense, the atom was already 'split'. The concept of directional valency implied that not only the compound, but also the atom itself possessed some kind of orientated structure.

The discovery of radioactivity, and particularly the identification of alpha particles as positively charged helium atoms and the discovery of the transmutation of chemical elements, was bound to lead to further thoughts and experiments on the inner structure of the atom.

In 1906 Rutherford, working at Montreal, discovered that a narrow beam of alpha particles was scattered through angles of up to 2 degrees by a thin sheet of mica placed in the beam. Rutherford commented, 'such a result brings out clearly the fact that the atoms of matter must be the seat of very intense electrical forces.'

After Rutherford had moved to the University of Manchester in 1907, his group of co-workers in the physics laboratories included H. Geiger and E. Marsden who examined the alpha particle scattering quantitatively (*Figure 7.1*). By means of a scintillation counter placed at an angle to the beam, they were able to record the frequency of alpha particle scattering at an angle ϕ greater than 90 degrees; this was found to be much greater than that calculated statistically for multiple scattering. Rutherford remarked that it was almost as incredible as if you fired a 15 in. shell at a piece of tissue paper and it came back and hit you. The amount of wide-angle scattering was found to be proportional to $\cosec^4 (\phi/2)$, the thickness of the foil, t, and the square of the atomic weight of the foil material. To explain this, Rutherford suggested that there must be a very intense central electrical charge (the nucleus) in an atom of the scattering foil. Most alpha particles pass through the atom itself without anything more than a slight deflection due to the electrostatic repulsion from the 'nucleus'. An occasional alpha particle approaches a nucleus at nearly head-on collision. Because the nuclear charge can be quite high, and the size of the alpha particle and of the nucleus are so small (order of 10^{-12} cm) even

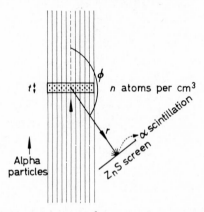

Figure 7.1. Measurement of the large angle scattering of alpha particles

by atomic standards (order of 10^{-8} cm), the electrostatic field can be high enough to cause even a total 'reflection' of an alpha particle travelling at 43,000,000 m/h (kinetic energy 7·68 MeV).

$$\text{Electrostatic force} = \frac{Ze \cdot E}{p^2}$$

where p is the distance of closest approach to the nucleus in any particular collision, E is the charge on the alpha particle and Ze is the nuclear charge.

The electrostatic force will be present whether the nucleus is positively *or* negatively charged—the only difference lies in the direction of deflection of the alpha particle, to left or to right (see *Figure 7.2*).

By conventional applied mathematics, Rutherford calculated that the fraction of particles scattered through an angle ϕ into the detector, compared with the number of particles which hit the foil, if both foil and detector have similar areas,

$$= \frac{nt}{16r^2} \operatorname{cosec}^4 (\phi/2) \cdot \frac{4Z^2e^2E^2}{M^2V^4}$$

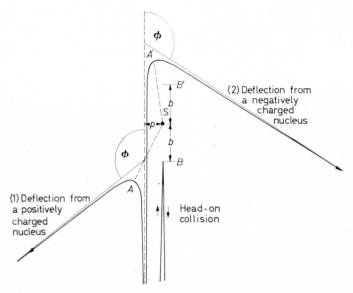

Figure 7.2. The geometry of large angle scattering of an alpha particle, A or B, from a nucleus S

Key: S = nucleus, as a point source; b = distance of separation for a head-on ($p = 0$) collision, at which the alpha particle is momentarily brought to rest (at B or B' according to whether the nucleus is $+$ ve or $-$ ve); p = perpendicular distance of direction of incoming particle, from S; ϕ = angular deflection (it may be shown: $\cot \phi/2 = 2p/b$, independent of charge)

where n = no. of atoms per cubic centimetre of the foil;

t = thickness of the foil;

r = distance of the scintillation detector from the centre of the foil;

Ze = charge on the nucleus;

E,M,V = the charge, mass and velocity of the alpha particle.

This calculation accounts for the experimental results of Geiger and Marsden, if we admit the assumption that the nuclear charge Ze is approximately proportional to the atomic weight.

J. J. Thompson had postulated in 1898 that an atom comprised electrons embedded in a sphere of positive electrification. Rutherford's work demonstrated that this was incorrect, and the positive charge was located in a nucleus which was extremely small compared with the atomic radius and which carried almost all the mass of the atom. This supported a theory of atomic structure which had been proposed by the Japanese physicist Nagaoka in 1904.

As it stands, this model does not tell us much about the exact value of the nuclear charge, nor about the arrangement of the electrons on the outer sphere, nor about the structure or composition of the nucleus itself. Furthermore, the model as it stands is unstable due to the electrostatic attraction between the nucleus and the electrons—they would be expected to be captured by the nucleus. Other lines of research and thought which were being pursued independently of Rutherford's work, fortunately bore fruit in time to supplement his theory of the nuclear atom. As Soddy has since commented, at about 1913 'all the evidence suddenly converged to make Rutherford's nuclear atom model universally acceptable.' We have now to consider these further lines of work.

An indication of the numerical value of the nuclear charge was obtained from the researches of Moseley at Cambridge in 1913, on X-ray spectra. Characteristic X-rays are emitted from a metal when it is used as the anticathode in a vacuum tube. By using the regular assembly of atoms in a crystal as a diffraction grating, it is possible to disperse the X-rays according to wavelength. It is found that the characteristic X-rays take the form of a simple line spectrum. An important part of this spectrum consists of a group of two doublets, the K lines $K\alpha_1$, $K\alpha_2$ and $K\beta_1$, $K\beta_2$. Moseley measured the wavelengths of these lines, using a crystal diffraction X-ray spectrometer, in the characteristic X-ray spectra of a large number of elements. For any given line, the frequency was proportional to $(Z - \sigma)^2$ where Z is the atomic number and σ is a constant, which for $K_\alpha = 1$. The atomic number represents the place of the particular element in the list of all the known elements arranged in the order of their atomic weight. Two qualifications were added to this generalization. Firstly, a place must be left in the list for any 'missing element', i.e. an element such as hafnium $(Z = 72)$, which had not been discovered in 1913 but which left an obvious gap in the Periodic Table. Secondly, nickel was to be placed *after* cobalt, i.e. in the reverse order of their atomic weights. This again pays attention to the accepted placing of these elements in the Periodic Table (*Figure 7.3*), which is based upon their chemical properties.

Period	1	2	3	4	5	6	7	8	0
1	H								He
2	Li	Be	B	C	N	O	F		Ne
3	Na	Mg	Al	Si	P	S	Cl		A
4	*A* K / *B* Cu	*A* Ca / *B* Zn	*A* Sc / *B* Ga	*A* Ti / *B* Ge	*A* V / *B* As	*A* Cr / *B* Se	*A* Mn / *B* Br	Fe Co Ni	Kr
5	Rb / Ag	Sr / Cd	Y / In	Zr / Sn	Nb / Sb	Mo / Te	Tc / I	Ru Rh Pd	Xe
6	Cs / Au	Ba / Hg	$_{57}$La to $_{71}$Lu / Tl	Hf / Pb	Ta / Bi	W / Po	Re / At	Os Ir Pt	Em
7	Fr	Ra	Ac $_{93}$Np to $_{103}$Lw	Th	Pa	U			

Figure 7.3. The Periodic Table of the Elements

71

Moseley concluded that the atomic number represented some fundamental quantity in the atom which increased by regular steps from element to element throughout the Periodic Table. So far we are dealing with empirical conclusions. It is, however, possible to suppose that Z might represent the number of positive charges on the nucleus (and also the number of electrons in the outer sphere when the atom is not ionized). The correctness of this guess is shown by the value of the hypothesis in accounting for known facts, e.g. the scattering of alpha particles, and predicting new ones.

An indication of the structure or composition of the nucleus comes from Soddy's Displacement Laws, if we combine them with Moseley's idea of the 'atomic number'. The loss of an alpha particle or of a beta particle from the nucleus produces a transmutation which corresponds with a change in Z of -2 units or of $+1$ unit respectively. This generalization was accounted for by using a model of the nucleus which contained A protons, where A is the numerical value of the atomic weight of the particular element, combined with $A - Z$ nuclear electrons—which serve only to neutralize an equal number of protons. The numerical value for the net positive charge on the nucleus is then

$$A - (A - Z) = Z$$

The alpha particle may be regarded as a helium nucleus, with $A = 4$, $Z = 2$, i.e. it is an assembly of four protons and two electrons, of net charge = two units. The loss of this fragment from the nucleus of uranium, for example, with $A = 238$, $Z = 92$, produces an isotope of the element $Z = 92 - 2 = 90$, i.e. thorium. The mass of this isotope is 238–4 = 234. This process is conveniently written as a 'nuclear reaction':

$$^{238}_{92}\text{U} \rightarrow {}^{4}_{2}\text{He} + {}^{234}_{90}\text{Th}$$

It is conventional to write the chemical symbol for an element, e.g. U, with the numerical values of A and of Z on the left-hand side and, respectively, slightly above and below the line of print.

The beta particle may be regarded as an electron which has left the nucleus, thus freeing one more proton to contribute to the nuclear charge. Thus $^{234}_{90}\text{Th}$ upon beta decay becomes an element of atomic number = 90 + 1 = 91, i.e. protoactinium. The mass of the protoactinium isotope remains 234, and the process may be written:

$$^{234}_{90}\text{Th} \rightarrow {}^{234}_{91}\text{Pa} + \beta$$

Experimentally it is found that ^{234}Pa also undergoes a beta decay, producing an isotope of uranium:

$$^{234}_{91}\text{Pa} \rightarrow {}^{234}_{92}\text{U} + \beta$$

The chain of processes from the common uranium isotope of mass 238 to one of mass 234 is the first part of the uranium decay series, which finally terminates at $^{206}_{82}$Pb.

Our model of the nuclear atom as it stands at this stage in our discussion contains two features which clash with the laws established in classical physics. Both of these concern the electrons. Neither the

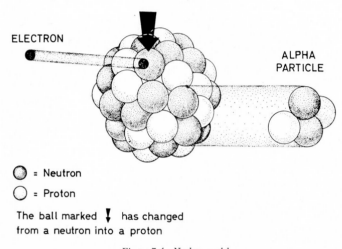

ELECTRON

ALPHA
PARTICLE

⬭ = Neutron

○ = Proton

The ball marked ↓ has changed from a neutron into a proton

Figure 7.4. Nuclear model

'outer' electrons on the surface of the atomic sphere nor the 'nuclear' electrons could be stable in the presence of the positive charges. This difficulty was solved in two stages. Niels Bohr at Manchester applied the Quantum Theory of Max Planck (1900) to the Ruther-ford atom and was able to account for the stability of the 'outer' electrons, in this key year of 1913. Then much later, in 1932, Chadwick at Cambridge recognized the experimental evidence for the existence of the neutron (see Chapter 8) and it was possible to construct a model of the nucleus which contained Z protons and $A - Z$ neutrons, with no nuclear electrons (*Figure 7.4*). The numerical value of A, sometimes called the Mass Number, represents the total number of protons *plus* neutrons in the nucleus. (The appearance of a beta particle in radioactive decay may be accounted for as a rare change of a neutron into a proton plus an escaping beta particle.) We have now to consider Bohr's model of the atom in more detail.

The Bohr Atom

Bohr put forward his model of the atom in order to account for the emission spectrum of hydrogen, i.e. the emission of light in the visible, ultra-violet and infra-red regions of the electro-magnetic spectrum, when hydrogen gas is energized—for example by the passage of an electrical discharge. This radiation is found on spectroscopic examination to consist of hundreds of fine lines, making up a pattern characteristic of hydrogen–helium and other gases each also having a distinct pattern, even more complex than that of hydrogen. Since 1885, Balmer and other physicists had devised mathematical equations to represent the patterns of the hydrogen spectrum, e.g. one particular series of lines (the Balmer series) have wave numbers according to the formula:

$$v' = R \left(\frac{1}{2^2} - \frac{1}{n^2} \right)$$

where $n = 3, 4, 5$, etc., $v' =$ the reciprocal of the wavelength in Ångström units and $R = 109, 677 \text{ cm}^{-1}$. More generally the whole pattern of lines can be fitted into the equation:

$$v' = R \left(\frac{1}{m^2} - \frac{1}{n^2} \right)$$

where m and n are integers and $n > m$. Of themselves, these equations did not contribute to our knowledge of the arrangement of the electrons in the atom. Bohr, however, had the insight to link one aspect of these equations with the Quantum Theory of radiation, propounded 13 years earlier by Planck and which had already proved successful in the mathematical treatment of such diverse topics as the radiation from heated solids, the specific heats of solids and the photoelectric effect. The Quantum Theory contained the postulate that electromagnetic radiation can only be emitted from a radiating source in discrete quantities or packets of energy (the 'quanta') and not in continuously variable amounts. In a sense this extends the idea of granular structure from matter (the atom) and electricity (the unit charge) to that of energy. The quantum (or 'atom' of energy) is hv where v is the frequency of the radiation and h is a constant. The 'size' of a quantum increases with the frequency of the radiation. In particular, the individual lines in the hydrogen spectrum will each be characterized by its own value of the quantum.

Bohr wedded the quantum theory of energy to his model of the individual atom of hydrogen and postulated that each single quantum in the radiation which comprised the hydrogen spectrum, came from a change of energy level of the 'outer' electrons in a single atom. It is possible to imagine a whole set of energy levels inside the hydrogen atom, such that transitions from higher to lower between various pairs of levels results in the emission of quanta of different size.

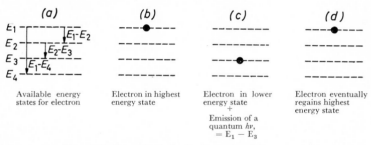

Figure 7.5. Energy levels for the electron in a hydrogen atom

In a large number of hydrogen atoms with a certain average thermal energy, there is always a small fraction which has energies well above the average (the energy distribution curve follows a Maxwellian function). If we suppose that some of this extra energy is 'concentrated' into the potential energy of an electron, we get the situation which is shown in a diagrammatic way in (b) and (d) of Figure 7.5. Bohr postulated that atoms containing electrons at such energy levels would occasionally emit a quantum of radiation to accompany a drop in electron energy level—in Figure 7.5, the decrease in energy level is $E_1 - E_3$. A sufficient number of atoms are undergoing this particular transition at any instant so that not just one quantum of any size $E_1 - E_3$ is emitted, but a continuous sequence of them, corresponding to one particular line in the hydrogen spectrum, of frequency $\nu = (E_1 - E_3)/h$. The large number of lines observed in this spectrum are due to the variety of possible combinations of energy levels, e.g. in Figure 7.5, quanta of 6 differing sizes could result from the following distinct decreases of energy level: $E_1 - E_2$, $E_1 - E_3$, $E_1 - E_4$, $E_2 - E_3$, $E_2 - E_4$ and $E_3 - E_4$.

These correspond with the successive terms in the empirical mathematical formulae due to Balmers and others,

$$\nu' = R \left(\frac{1}{m^2} - \frac{1}{n^2} \right)$$

$$\nu' = \frac{\nu}{c}$$

where c = velocity of light.

Therefore

$$\nu' = \frac{E_1 - E_3}{hc}$$

where

$$E_1 \propto \frac{1}{m^2} \quad \text{and} \quad E_3 \propto \frac{1}{n^2}$$

the selection of the pair of energy levels E_1, E_2, E_3, E_4 depending upon the values of the integers m and n.

We have deliberately presented the Bohr model of the atom in a rather abstract form, without so far relating the energy levels of the electrons to any of their physical properties such as distance from the nucleus (coulombic energy), velocity in movement around the nucleus (kinetic energy), spinning motion (rotational energy), etc. Logically this forms a second phase of the development of the model. In fact Bohr included this second phase as an integral part of his theory, and he put forward a particular dynamic model of the electrons in elliptical orbits about the nucleus. More recently, the mathematical ideas of wave mechanics have supplied a less Newtonian interpretation of the electronic energy states, making it possible to give an exact treatment to the chemical problems of valency, including the orientation of valency in three dimensions. The basic ideas of quantized radiation and of discrete electronic energy levels—the first phase of the theory—are still applicable, whatever model we adopt to account for the electronic energy states. An outline of Bohr's orbital electron model is included here, with the warning that for the purposes of more advanced study it will be necessary to replace it by the wave mechanical model.

Bohr's Orbital Electrons

Rutherford's 'nuclear' model of the atom had set the electrons, in sufficient number to balance the positive charge on the nucleus, rotating in orbits on the surface of the atomic sphere. Unfortunately, the classical physics showed that a rotating charge in an electric field would lose energy as electromagnetic radiation, and the electron would spiral in eventually to collide with the nucleus. During this process a continuous spectrum of electromagnetic radiation would be emitted. Bohr accepted that the

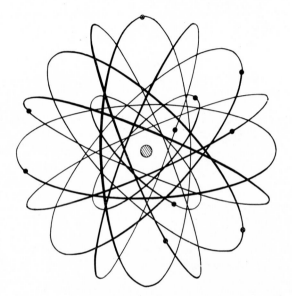

Figure 7.6. Bohr's atomic model

electrons were in planetary motion in orbits about the nucleus (*Figure 7.6*). His new postulate was, that for any electron, a limited number of orbits were available—these being characterized by an integer n, which Bohr associated with r, the radius of the orbit, which for simplicity we here regard as circular:

$$r \propto n^2$$

The energy of the electron in one of these orbits is the sum of the kinetic and potential energies:

$$E = mv^2/2 - Ze \cdot e/r \tag{7.1}$$

where the second term represents the coulombic energy of attraction between the nucleus and the electron.

The acceleration towards the centre of a circular orbit is v^2/r, and this is supplied by the force of electrostatic attraction Ze^2/r^2

$$\frac{mv^2}{r} = \frac{Ze^2}{r^2}$$

whence

$$v^2 = \frac{Ze^2}{m \cdot r} \tag{7.2}$$

Substituting for v^2 in equation 7.1,

$$E = \frac{Ze^2}{2r} - \frac{Ze^2}{r} = -\frac{Ze^2}{2r}$$

Each orbit with its characteristic radius, corresponds to a definite energy level. The negative sign before the expression $Ze^2/2r$ in the above equation expresses the fact that one would need to supply energy to the system in order to remove the electron to an infinite distance from the nucleus, that is, to a state having zero potential energy.

Bohr further supposed that an electron normally remained in one particular orbit without the uptake or emission of radiant energy (despite the conclusions of classical physics), but that occasionally it might undergo an instantaneous transition to another orbit. In the case that the second orbit was of lower energy than the first (i.e. that the second orbit lay nearer to the nucleus) then a quantum of energy was emitted as electromagnetic radiation: $h\nu = E_1 - E_2$ (cf. *Figure 7.5*). Since $E = -\dfrac{Ze^2}{2r}$ and $r \propto n^2$ then

$$h\nu = E_1 - E_2 = K\left(\frac{1}{n_2^2} - \frac{1}{n_1^2}\right)$$

or

$$\nu' = R\left(\frac{1}{n_2^2} - \frac{1}{n_1^2}\right), \text{ where } \nu' = \nu/c$$

Bohr was successful in calculating the absolute value of the constant R as 109,737 cm^{-1}, in good agreement with the experimentally determined value, which was 109,677 cm^{-1} (p. 74).

This simple dynamic model of planetary electrons in circular orbits accounts for the main lines in the hydrogen spectrum. In order to account for the splitting of the lines into groups of 2 or 4 and to account for the effects of strong magnetic and electrical fields upon the spectra, it is necessary to elaborate the theory—even for hydrogen, but particularly so for the heavier elements. In order completely to define the energy level of an orbital electron, not one integer (n) but *four* numbers are required. These are called the principal, azimuthal, magnetic and spin quantum numbers, and the principal quantum number is identical with Bohr's integer (n). Originally these numbers were associated with physical properties of the electron such as the two parameters of an elliptic orbit, the angular momentum and the spin of the electron, but this crude picture is now discredited in favour of wave mechanical treatment. Broadly speaking, the electron is now regarded not as a localized particle but as an 'electron cloud' smeared out in three dimensions around the nucleus and represented mathematically by the general wave equations of Schrödinger, which require four separate integers —we may for convenience continue to call these the principal, azimuthal, magnetic and spin quantum numbers—for a specific solution to fit the case of any one particular electron. The four quantum numbers are not completely independent of one another; arising from the mathematical solutions of the wave equations it is found that they are required to obey the following rules:

Principal q.n. . . . any positive integer.

Azimuthal q.n. . . . zero or any positive integer which remains less than the p.q.n.

Magnetic q.n. . . . zero or any positive or negative integer whose magnitude with disregard of algebraic sign is equal to or less than the a.q.n.

Spin q.n. . . . . . one of two alternative values, which are conventionally written as $+\frac{1}{2}$ and $-\frac{1}{2}$ respectively.

It is profitable to conduct the apparently abstract mathematical exercise of setting out the number of different possible combinations of the four quantum numbers, as shown in the following example:

How many sets of quantum numbers are possible in a case where the principal quantum number is fixed at 2?

$$\text{Principal} = 2$$
$$\text{Azimuthal} = 1 \quad \text{or} \quad 0$$
$$\text{Magnetic} = 1, 0 \quad \text{or} \quad -1$$
$$\text{Spin} = +\tfrac{1}{2} \quad \text{or} \quad -\tfrac{1}{2}$$

The number of possible sets, e.g. $(2, 1, -1, +\frac{1}{2})$ $(2, 1, -1, -\frac{1}{2})$, etc. is 8.

The number of possible sets increases rapidly with the value of the principal quantum number (Table 7.1).

At this point our mathematical exercise yields a set of numbers which are closely connected with the Periodic Table; they are in fact the maximum numbers of separate energy levels in successive shells (K, L, M, N) of the six members of the inert gas series, Group 0 of the Periodic Table.

It is generally accepted that the chemical reactions of the elements are a consequence of displacements and combinations of the outer electrons. This view goes back to G. N. Lewis of the University of California who used it in teaching from 1902 and published a notable paper *The Atom and the Molecule* in 1916. The quantum numbers of wave mechanics are highly significant in determining the chemical behaviour of an element, because they define the number of energy states which are available for occupation by

Table 7.1.

Principal quantum No.	Number of sets
1	2
2	8
3	18
4	32
5	50
6	72

electrons. There are two ways of looking at this. We can consider these energy states as empty except for one particular electron and we can concentrate our attention on the transitions and quantum radiation (or absorption) of this electron, the approach followed in considering the hydrogen spectrum. Alternatively, we may consider the filling up of the available energy levels by means of successive electrons until the atom accommodates the maximum number and there is no vacant energy level. Chemically, this results in a very unreactive element and we may try to explain this fact in terms of the special stability of a completed set (or 'shell') of electronic energy levels. G. N. Lewis pointed out that the chemical evidence seemed to require a special stability attached to a group of eight electrons in the outermost shell. More commonly, elements have not the exact number of electrons which are necessary to complete a 'shell', and their chemical reactions are then 'driven' by the necessity of losing or acquiring one or more electrons in order to attain to, or to revert to, a stable 'shell', i.e. an electronic configuration similar to that of one of the inert gases in Group 0. (Table 7.2.)

Alternatively, elements could gain a stable 'octet' by the mutual sharing of one or more outer electrons between two atoms of the same or different elements as in chlorine gas, Cl—Cl, which is a typical non-polar or 'covalent' compound.

In all electron shells after the first and second, not only the complete shell but also certain *partially* completed sets of energy levels confer an 'inert' chemical character upon the element, as in A, Kr, Xe and Em. The set of eight occupied electron energy levels is particularly important in the shell of highest principal quantum number. When this octet sub-shell is complete, as in argon, the successive incorporation of further electrons in the succeeding elements K, Ca, Sc takes place to some extent into the next shell

Table 7.2. Electronic Configurations for the Inert Gases

Electron shells						Atomic number
K	L	M	N	O	P	
2						2 (He)
2	8					10 (Ne)
2	8	8				18 (A)
2	8	18	8			36 (Kr)
2	8	18	18	8		54 (Xe)
2	8	18	32	18	8	86 (Em)

(in this example, this will be the shell of principal quantum number 4) *before* the penultimate shell is completed from the octet to the maximum, which in our particular example is 18. The recognition of the importance of a completed octet in the highest shell involves the recognition that the inert gases follow the sequence shown in Table 7.2, which makes their atomic numbers 2, 10, 18, 36, 54, 86 and not simply the sequence of completed outer shells, which, from Table 7.1, would be 2, 10, 28, 60, 110, 182.

Bohr himself introduced this extension of his theory in 1921 in order to explain the atomic numbers of the inert gases following neon. Simultaneously, the physical chemist Bury at Aberystwyth introduced a similar concept in order to explain the detailed structure of the Periodic Table which had been derived from experimental chemistry, e.g. the occurrence of the 'transition elements' from titanium to copper and again in Group 8, and of the rare earths.

Such chemical facts as the variable valency of the transition elements, e.g. copper, with a valency of 1 or 2; iron, with a valency of 2 or 3; chromium, with a valency of 2, 3 or 6; led Bury to suppose that two or more states may have closely similar energies, e.g. copper as:

$$2, 8, 18, 1 \qquad \text{or} \qquad 2, 8, 17, 2$$

ionizing to

$$(2, 8, 18)^+ \qquad \text{or} \qquad (2, 8, 17)^{++}$$

cuprous ion   cupric ion

The set of electron orbits represented on the right hand is supposed to be slightly more stable than the alternative set, in order to account for the chemical fact that cupric salts are stable in aqueous solution whereas cuprous salts are rapidly oxidized by dissolved oxygen. The completed electron shells of lower principal quantum number, much less the structure of the nucleus of the atom, have very little influence upon the chemical properties of the element.

Table 7.3. Relative Stabilities of Nuclei of Mass 234

Protons	Neutrons	At. wt.	Element	Radioactive properties
90	144	234	Thorium	24·1 day, β
91	143	234	Protactinium	1·2 min, β
92	142	234	Uranium	$2 \cdot 5 \times 10^5$ y, α

By contrast, the nuclear structure is all-important in the study of radioactivity, whereas the *chemical* state of an element such as radium is completely immaterial in considering its half-life or the nature and energy of its disintegrations. By virtue of the success of numerical patterns of electron energy levels in the interpretation of chemical properties, and because a pattern of nuclear energy levels is revealed by alpha, beta and gamma spectroscopy, e.g. *Figure 4.6*, it is natural to inquire whether the arrangement of protons and neutrons in the nucleus follows a numerical pattern, with finite 'shells', which might interpret the facts of radioactivity. Such facts would have to include the variations of nuclear stability between nuclei of similar mass shown in Table 7.3.

The data to be correlated is greatly extended by the inclusion, not only of the several hundred *artificial* radioactive isotopes, but also by the relative isotopic abundances of the *stable* elements, e.g. magnesium, $Z = 12$, has *three* stable isotopes, of weight 24, 25 and 26, whereas its neighbours of odd atomic numbers, 11 (sodium) and 13 (aluminium) are mono-isotopic.

The stable nuclei usually have:

(*a*) An excess of neutrons over protons, amounting to 1 or 2 neutrons for the lighter elements, rising to 44 excess neutrons for one of the stable isotopes of lead.

(*b*) An even number of neutrons.

(*c*) Certain proton and neutron numbers which appear to confer a particular stability, e.g. the numbers $Z = 2, 8, 20, 28, 50, 82$ and $N = 2, 8, 20, 28, 50, 82, 126$ are associated with an abnormally large number of *stable* nuclei or else radioactive nuclei of *longer* half-life than might otherwise be expected. These empirical observations can partly be interpreted in terms of closed shells of protons and/or neutrons in the nucleus, like the chemical details of the Periodic Table in terms of closed shells of electrons.

The Nuclear Shell or Independent Particle theory considers each 'nucleon' (proton or neutron) to occupy a quantum state under the influence of the potential energy field due to the sum of all the other nucleons. Individual interactions between one nucleon and another are assumed to be weak. The laws of force which govern the change in potential energy with a shift in the position of the nucleon are not so simple as the coulombic law which governs the interaction between the nucleus and an orbital electron. Again, the energy levels for a given value of the principal quantum number are greatly affected by what is called 'coupling' between the orbital angular momentum and the spin. In 1949, Mrs. M. G. Mayer in U.S.A. and (independently) O. Haxel, J. H. D. Jensen and H. E. Suess in Germany showed that with certain assumptions the Nuclear Shell theory accounted for the numbers 2, 8, 20, 50, 82 and 126 as the number of separate quantum states in successive shells. The theory does not account for certain other properties of the nucleus such as the magnetic quadrupole moment, which is a measure of the slight elongation of the nucleus in a direction parallel to (positive quadrupole moment) or at right angles to (negative quadrupole moment) the axis of spin. Values for the quadrupole moment can be deduced from measurements of the behaviour of nuclei in magnetic fields and from the fine structure of optical and microwave spectra.

The anomalies are particularly marked when the nuclear shells are only partially filled, and in such cases the Collective or Unified Model can better account for the high observed quadrupole moments. This theory has been developed by A. Bohr (son of Niels Bohr) since 1951, and it includes the assumption that the outer shells of the nucleus behave as a liquid, in which tidal motion can occur.

The Collective Model bears some resemblance to the Liquid Drop model due to N. Bohr and others since 1936. This earliest of the models of nuclear structure assumed that the individual nucleus interacted with one another very strongly, so that any increase in the kinetic and potential energy of the nucleus, as by the incorporation of an incoming particle, say an alpha particle or a neutron, was rapidly shared out amongst the separate nucleons, one or more of which might in consequence be ejected from the 'compound nucleus'. This theory accounts for certain features of nuclear reactions, including nuclear fission (see Chapter 9).

Finally, we have to consider the mechanism of the processes of radioactive decay. We have studied the nature of alpha and beta particles and of gamma rays. By what mechanism are the alpha and the beta particles respectively ejected from the nucleus with high kinetic energies? (The release of gamma rays is a secondary process from an excited state of the residual nucleus, see Chapter 4, p. 43.)

The ejection of a particle from a given nucleus of a radioactive isotope appears to be at random: the laws of radioactive decay (Chapter 5) are statistical summaries of the behaviour of large numbers of atoms. There appears at present to be no way of predicting that one particular nucleus of a radioactive species will or will not eject a particle during a specified interval of time (this interval being short compared with the half-life).

According to G. Gamow and (independently) R. W. Gurney and E. U. Condon in 1928, the wave mechanical model of matter can be used to deal with the behaviour of an alpha particle inside the nucleus, which according to classical theory cannot escape because it has an energy of less than 25 MeV, the so-called 'barrier' to escape. The classical theory would visualize the escape as an either/or process. *Either*, the alpha particle has at least 25 MeV of available energy, and escapes, *or* it has insufficient energy and remains in the nucleus. Wave mechanics show that in place of either/or we can visualize a 'probability function' such that an alpha particle with *less* than 25 MeV has a small but definable chance of 'tunnelling through' the barrier. The chances increase, of course with energy and that is why the most highly energetic alpha particles usually emerge from isotopes of very short half-life [e.g. thorium-C' (polonium-212), half-life 0·3 μs, alpha energy 8·78 MeV, compared with thorium-232, half-life 1·39 × 10^{10} y, alpha energy 3·99 MeV.]

The emission of a beta particle (together with a neutrino) from a nucleus depends upon the transition of a neutron into a proton. E. Fermi, in 1934, applied wave mechanics to derive the probability of escape from the nucleus, of a beta particle with specified energy. It was necessary for him to include the 'neutrino' in his calculations, to account for the fact that most of the observed beta particles have *less* than the maximum energy (cf. Chapter 3, p. 32).

8

ARTIFICIAL RADIOACTIVITY

Radioactivity had been discovered in 1896 as a property of the elements uranium and thorium. Both these elements were already reasonably familiar to the chemist and were manufactured by the ton as industrial materials: uranium oxide as a yellow colouring matter for china, thorium oxide as a constituent of incandescent gas mantles. Additionally, three completely new elements, polonium, radium and actinium, were discovered by means of their radioactive properties. It was eventually found possible to include these new elements, together with the newly discovered radioactive isotopes of lead, bismuth and thallium and also the short-lived radioactive element, radon, within the framework of three natural disintegration series of which the parents were uranium-238, uranium-235 and thorium-232 (*Figure 6.4*). In the course of these investigations, the phenomena of radioactivity were related to the spontaneous disintegration of atomic nuclei. No laboratory process whether a treatment with powerful chemical reagents or an application of physical forces such as heat, electrification, pressure, etc., had been found to produce radioactivity in an element (more strictly in an isotope) which was naturally stable, nor to change in any way the half-life of a radioactive element. For example, lengthy experiments were made to measure the disintegration rate of radium in a variety of different chemical compounds and also under extremes of temperature and pressure, without producing any significant change outside the limits of experimental error (say 1 in 1000).

A new vista opened up in 1919 when it was found to be possible to *initiate* nuclear disintegrations by laboratory operations. The key to this breakthrough was the use of a physical agent which (*a*) could approach very near to the nucleus, (*b*) possessed an energy comparable with the energies released in natural nuclear disintegrations, and (*c*) was able to change the balance of proton and neutrons in the nucleus.

Not surprisingly, the alpha particle, which had already been used by Rutherford to probe into the heart of the atom in the scattering experiments (p. 67) and which had led him to the nuclear model of the atom, proved to be the required agent.

Rutherford studied the detailed effects of a beam of alpha particles upon hydrogen and other gases. It was, of course, well known that the gas became ionized, and one would expect that free electrons and positively charged ions of the gaseous atoms or molecules would be released. It would be possible for an alpha particle to lose a high proportion of its kinetic energy in a collision with a hydrogen molecule, far more than the 35 eV or so required for ionization, and the energy would be passed on to the positive hydrogen ion. Rutherford did in fact detect fast moving hydrogen ions (protons) which left the ionization chamber (*Figure 8.1*) through a 'window' of metal foil which was just thick enough to stop the residual alpha particles. They could be identified as protons (*a*) by their maximum

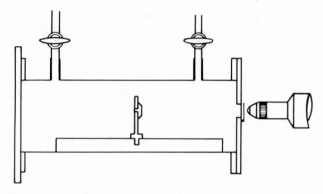

Figure 8.1. Rutherford's apparatus for bombarding gases with alpha particles

(From Rutherford, Chadwick and Ellis *Radiations from Radioactive Substances:* Cambridge University Press, London, 1930)

range in aluminium foil which was equivalent to 28 cm of air; (*b*) by the relative brightness of the scintillations produced on a zinc sulphide screen—these resembled the known scintillations caused by protons rather than by alpha particles; (*c*) by deflection experiments in magnetic and electrical fields.

In 1919, Rutherford published the results of experiments in which the gas nitrogen was used to replace hydrogen. Surprisingly, some fast protons were still detected, even when all possible precautions had been taken to exclude any traces of impurities which would contain hydrogen. From the results so far obtained, Rutherford wrote 'it is difficult to avoid the conclusion that the long-range atoms arising from collision of alpha particles with nitrogen are not nitrogen atoms but probably atoms of hydrogen . . ... If this be the case, we must conclude that the nitrogen atom is being disintegrated under the intense forces developed in close collision with a swift alpha particle. . . .'

In some way the bombardment of nitrogen by alpha particles had released not only positively charged N but also a small number of protons, estimated at one proton per hundred thousand alpha particles. The occurrence was so infrequent that it was not possible to show what happened to the alpha particle itself in this process. This information, also the correlation of the emission of protons with a nuclear disintegration of a nitrogen atom:

$$^{14}_{7}N + ^{4}_{2}He \rightarrow ^{17}_{8}O + ^{1}_{1}H$$

came later from the work of Blackett. Using a cloud chamber, it was possible to photograph the tracks of alpha particles in air or in nitrogen. Occasionally these tracks showed evidence of an elastic collision between an alpha particle and a nucleus of oxygen or nitrogen, with a deflected alpha particle and a new dense track due to the high speed recoil of the nucleus. Very infrequently, evidence was obtained of a different type of collision (*Figure 8.2*) where the alpha track disappears completely, leaving a dense recoil track and a thin extended track. From experience of the tracks of various charged particles in the cloud chamber, it is possible to characterize the energy, velocity and nature of a particle from photographs of its track (similar techniques have since become very important in the study of particle tracks in photographic emulsions). Further, it is often possible to deduce quite a lot about a nuclear disintegration from cloud chamber (or photographic emulsion) measurements of the velocity, energy and angular displacement of the incident and emergent particles. Blackett's photographs of cloud chamber tracks agreed with the representation of the interaction of alpha particles with nitrogen to produce protons as:

$$^{14}_{7}N + ^{4}_{2}He \rightarrow ^{17}_{8}O + ^{1}_{1}H$$

The element nitrogen has been transmuted, on a minute scale, to a rare stable isotope of the element oxygen. The isotopic composition of normal atmospheric oxygen is:

O–16   99·759 per cent
O–17   0·037 per cent
O–18   0·204 per cent

The equation written above is an example of a nuclear reaction, produced at will in the laboratory. Later, 14 light elements were found by Rutherford and Chadwick (1920–24) to release fast protons (in very low yield) upon bombardment with alpha particles. The 'man-made nuclear reaction' in each case remains dependent upon the use of alpha particles which are themselves the product of a natural, nuclear disintegration.

It was not until 1932 that it was found to be possible as it were

Figure 8.2. Alpha tracks in (a) helium and (b) nitrogen gases
(From Rutherford, Chadwick and Ellis *Radiations from Radioactive Substances:* Cambridge University Press, London, 1930)

to dispense entirely with natural radioactive sources and to produce one's own projectiles. This had always been theoretically possible, if a charged particle such as the hydrogen or helium nucleus could be accelerated to a sufficiently high velocity. In principle, this can be done by applying an electric field, for example a potential difference of one million volts, to a proton, which will accelerate it to a velocity of about one-twentieth of the velocity of light, when its kinetic energy becomes 1 MeV. Even this energy is smaller than that of the alpha particles which are released by spontaneous radio-active decay (4–9 MeV). The practical hindrance to the use of accelerated projectiles lay in the very high voltages required, which were greater than the highest voltages then commonly used in laboratories (up to 50,000 V for X-ray tubes). Cockcroft and Walton, working at the Cavendish Laboratory, Cambridge, in 1932 con-structed a high voltage generator to give a total potential difference of 800,000 V, and applied this to the acceleration of a stream of protons down a long tube. The accelerated protons, of maximum energy 0·8 MeV, were caused to strike a thin sample of lithium metal. A scintillation screen placed on the far side of the lithium showed a number of bright scintillations due to alpha particles. The nuclear reaction proceeding in the lithium was shown to be:

$$\tfrac{7}{3}\text{Li} + \tfrac{1}{1}\text{H} \rightarrow 2\tfrac{4}{2}\text{He}$$

This is particularly interesting because the roles of the proton and the alpha particle, as incident and emergent particle, respectively, are reversed compared with Rutherford's earlier work. This particular reaction was a happy choice on the part of Cockcroft and Walton, for it only required relatively low proton energies—some alpha particles were released even at 130,000 V applied potential. This is because the nucleus of lithium ($\tfrac{7}{3}$Li) is potentially unstable. What is important in nuclear reactions is that the com-bined energy of the nuclei and particles on the left-hand side of the equation shall reach the threshold of potential energy required for reaction (corresponding to the activation energy in a chemical reaction).

More usually, the nuclear reactions which can in principle be brought about by protons, deuterons, alpha particles, etc., require that the incident particle has an energy considerably higher than the 0·8 MeV used by Cockcroft and Walton. Physicists and electrical engineers over the last thirty years have designed and built 'particle accelerators' of great ingenuity, complexity and cost in the search for higher and higher energies. The cyclotron, linear accelerator, van der Graaf machine, and synchrocyclotron now furnish energies of up to 50 BeV (1 BeV = 10^3 MeV). Some recently quoted figures (1961) are:

C.E.R.N. (Geneva) proton synchrotron	25 BeV
Brookhaven National Laboratory, Long Island, U.S.A. alternating gradient synchrotron	30 BeV

Rutherford High Energy Laboratory (Harwell)
proton synchrotron   7 BeV
Leningrad U.S.S.R. synchrophasotron   50 BeV
Stanford University, U.S.A. electron linear accelerator   45 BeV

Even these energies are small compared with those of some of the primary particles of the cosmic rays, which are found to enter the earth's atmosphere from outer space. The primary particles are fast moving protons and other positively charged atoms of atomic number up to 28, and energies of up to 10^9 BeV (though their mean energy is about 10 BeV) and enter into nuclear reactions with the earth's atmosphere to form showers of secondary particles, such as mesons. (A meson is a positive, negative or neutral particle, of mass intermediate between that of an electron and a proton.)

We have now to return to the state of nuclear research just before the experiments of Cockcroft and Walton in 1932. Various scientists were still following up Rutherford's use of alpha particles as projectiles to bring about nuclear changes. These experiments had two important results: each derived from the following-up of apparent anomalies. One was the discovery of artificial radioactivity: the other was the discovery of the neutron.

Frédéric Joliot and Irène Curie (Irène was the daughter of Marie and Pierre Curie) were investigating the action of alpha rays upon beryllium, to examine the strange penetrating radiation found by Bothe and Becker (see p. 91). They allowed the alpha particles from polonium to pass from their container through a 'window' of very thin aluminium foil. It was found that the aluminium became radioactive, and that the radioactivity could still be detected when the aluminium was removed from exposure to the alpha rays. The radioactivity was not a deposit from a gaseous emanation, for polonium is not like radium in this respect. Upon removal from the alpha rays, the aluminium radioactivity decayed with a half-life of 3 min. By dissolving the radioactive aluminium in caustic soda and then carrying out rapid chemical separations in the presence of 'carriers', it may be shown that the radioactivity is associated not with the aluminium but with the element, phosphorus. The nuclear reactions may be represented:

$$\ce{^{27}_{13}Al} + \ce{^{4}_{2}He} \rightarrow \ce{^{30}_{15}P} + \ce{^{1}_{0}n}$$

$$\ce{^{30}_{15}P}(t_{\frac{1}{2}} = 3 \text{ min}) \rightarrow \ce{^{30}_{14}Si} + \beta^+$$

Not only aluminium but also boron and magnesium were transmuted by alpha particles into artificial radioactive isotopes, of nitrogen ($^{13}_{7}$N, $t_{\frac{1}{2}} = 11$ min), and silicon ($^{27}_{14}$Si, $t_{\frac{1}{2}} = 4$ sec) respectively. In each case the new radioactive elements were positron emitters, and decayed to give stable isotopes of elements which were one unit lower in atomic number. This is an interesting extension of one of Soddy's Displacement Laws (the emission of a beta particle gives an element which is one unit *higher* in atomic number). The positron, or positive electron, has the same mass as the electron, and differs only in the polarity of its electrical charge. This particle had already been detected in the cosmic rays by means of photographs of tracks in cloud chambers in the presence of a magnetic field (Anderson, and, independently, Blackett, 1932).

The discovery of artificial radioactivity has made it possible to prepare in the laboratory, radioactive isotopes of every element in the Periodic Table and we are no longer limited in our study of radioactivity to those elements which occur naturally in one or more radioactive isotopes. The use of a wide variety of radioactive isotopes to assist in research work in physics, chemistry, biology and in practical problems of industry, agriculture and medicine is now of such importance that it will receive separate treatment in Chapter 11.

We ought, however, to mention here that the most important method of preparation of artificial radioactive isotopes was discovered by Fermi at Rome in 1934, using neutrons, and we must now deal with the discovery of the release of neutrons from the beryllium nucleus by bombardment with alpha particles.

Bothe and Becker in 1930, investigated in detail the action of alpha particles upon beryllium, and found that a radiation was emitted which was even more penetrating than the fast-moving protons which Rutherford had detected as a product of the action of alpha particles upon nitrogen and other elements. The new radiation was not completely absorbed even by thick lead screens; 2·5 cm of lead reduced the intensity only by a factor of two. Bothe and Becker concluded that the radiations were gamma rays of very high energy (compare 1 MeV gamma rays, which are reduced in intensity by a factor of two, by 0·9 cm of lead). Frédéric and Irène Joliot-Curie discovered that these highly penetrating radiations were comparatively easily absorbed, however, in substances such as paraffin wax and water. In order to absorb the radiation, a substance had to contain hydrogen atoms, and it was further shown that during the absorption process, fast-moving protons were released, of maximum energy 4·5 MeV. It was difficult to account for the release of energetic protons if the penetrating radiations were gamma rays.

Chadwick in 1932 pointed out that the facts were readily

understood, without discarding the laws of conservation of energy and of momentum, if the penetrating radiation consisted of *particles* of mass nearly equal to that of the proton and with no net electrical charge. Such a particle, the *neutron*, had been suggested in 1920 by W. D. Harkins in U.S.A., by O. Masson in Australia and by Rutherford at Cambridge, but no one had been able to detect it experimentally. Chadwick also applied the cloud chamber technique to study the new radiation, as he had previously done to study the interaction of alpha particles with the nucleus of the nitrogen atom. The penetrating radiation did not produce any direct tracks in the cloud chamber, but it could occasionally be detected indirectly by the unique tracks which were produced when it interacted with the nucleus of a light element such as nitrogen. The photographs showed a short heavy track (like the recoil track previously shown in *Figure 8.2*), together with the track of an alpha particle. These were interpreted by Chadwick as being the tracks of the emergent particles after a nuclear reaction between the neutron and the nucleus of nitrogen:

$$^{14}_{7}\text{N} + {}^{1}_{0}\text{n} \rightarrow {}^{4}_{2}\text{He} + {}^{11}_{5}\text{B}$$

The heavy track is due to the recoil of the boron nucleus. The reason that the neutron itself gives no track and shows such penetration into, say, lead, is that it does not ionize the atoms of the material in its path, and passes through the extranuclear electrons. The lack of an electric charge on the neutron may be shown by its failure to be deflected by a magnetic or electrical field. Its mass may be deduced from considerations of the conservation of energy and of momentum, as applied to nuclear reactions.

Mass of neutron = 1·009 units
Mass of proton   = 1·008 units
Mass of electron = 0·0005 units

[on the physical atomic weight standard (oxygen = 16·000)].

The nuclear reaction between alpha particles and the nucleus of beryllium, studied by Bothe and Becker, may now be written:

$$^{9}_{4}\text{Be} + {}^{4}_{2}\text{He} \rightarrow {}^{12}_{6}\text{C} + {}^{1}_{0}\text{n}$$

The neutrons emerging from this reaction are now known to have energies of at least 5·5 MeV. The function of hydrogen-containing materials in absorbing these fast neutrons is twofold. First, the neutrons lose energy by elastic collision with hydrogen atoms, until after several successive collisions the neutrons are travelling at speeds no greater than those of the random thermal motion of gas molecules at room temperature—they are then called 'slow neutrons' (energy about 0·02 eV) and the slowing down process is known as the 'moderation' of fast neutrons. Hydrogeneous materials are good 'moderators'. Secondly, the slow neutrons enter into a nuclear reaction with hydrogen, carbon, oxygen or other elements which are present in the absorber, e.g.

$$\ce{^1_1H + ^1_0n -> ^2_1H}$$

In the nuclear reaction which is represented above, hydrogen is converted into its heavier isotope, deuterium, without any release of particles. In such reactions there is, however, usually a balance of energy to be released, and this appears partly as the recoil energy of the deuterium nucleus and partly as the radiant energy of gamma rays.

Enrico Fermi, who in 1934 was Professor of Theoretical Physics at Rome University, read the paper by the Joliot-Curies on artificial radioactivity, and decided to try to produce similar nuclear reactions by using neutrons rather than alpha particles as projectiles. With his colleagues, E. Segré and E. Amaldi, he obtained neutrons from a mixture of beryllium powder and the alpha-emitting gas radon, contained in a sealed glass tube:

$$\ce{^9_4Be + ^4_2He -> ^{12}_6C + ^1_0n}$$

Samples of suitable compounds of practically every element in the Periodic Table were placed near the neutron source, and were then removed to another laboratory in the same building to be tested for beta and gamma activity with a Geiger counter (the gamma rays from the radon in the neutron source would have caused a high 'background' response in the Geiger counter if it were placed in the same room). Enrico's wife, Laura, relates how an important visitor to the laboratories was surprised when Fermi and Amaldi 'both in dirty grey coats, tore madly by him, holding strange objects in their hands', for on that occasion, haste was essential, and the time to cover the length of the corridor (from the neutron source to the Geiger counter) had to be reduced by swift running. During the spring of 1934, the neutron irradiation of the first seven elements in the Periodic Table produced no measurable radioactivity. The eighth element, fluorine, brought success. A very short-lived beta activity was detected:

$$\ce{^{19}_9F + ^1_0n -> ^{20}_9F} \xrightarrow{t_{\frac{1}{2}}=11 \text{ sec}} \ce{^{20}_{10}Ne} \text{ (stable)} + \beta$$

Most of the remaining elements of the Periodic Table showed a neutron-induced radioactivity. A further example is that of silver, where a mixture of two radioactive isotopes was produced, differing in half-life:

$$^{107}_{47}\text{Ag} + ^{1}_{0}\text{n} \rightarrow ^{108}_{47}\text{Ag} \xrightarrow{t_{\frac{1}{2}}=2\cdot3 \text{ min}} {}^{108}_{48}\text{Cd (stable)} + \beta$$

$$^{109}_{47}\text{Ag} + ^{1}_{0}\text{n} \rightarrow ^{110}_{47}\text{Ag} \xrightarrow{t_{\frac{1}{2}}=24 \text{ sec}} {}^{110}_{48}\text{Cd (stable)} + \beta$$

In October, 1934, the importance of this new method of preparation of radioactive isotopes was accentuated by an accidental discovery. B. Pontecorvo and E. Amaldi were irradiating a cylinder of silver, which fitted around the neutron source, and the complete assembly was placed inside a lead box (to protect the scientists from the gamma rays of radon). They found that the radioactivity produced in the silver appeared to depend upon the exact place where the assembly was placed inside the lead box. Further experiments were made with the assembly taken *out of* the lead box, and finally, with Fermi and Rasetti, the experimenters placed the assembly inside a hole in a large block of paraffin wax. The presence of the paraffin increased the artificially induced radioactivity of silver up to one hundred times. The experiment was repeated with the assembly placed under water (in a goldfish pond!), and the water also increased the radioactivity. Fermi correctly deduced that the function of lead, paraffin wax or water was to slow down the fast neutrons from the radon–beryllium source, i.e. the 'moderation' of fast neutrons. Materials which contain hydrogen are particularly effective (Table 9.2).

The slow neutrons are particularly effective in bringing about nuclear reactions, for three reasons. First, because they are neutral they can approach very near the nucleus without being repelled by coulombic forces. Secondly, their slow speeds permit of a reasonable probability of capture by the nucleus before they pass out of effective range. Thirdly, the capture of an extra neutron by a nucleus disturbs the balance of protons and neutrons and creates a nuclear instability which may result in the ejection of a proton, alpha particle, positron, or electron.

The process used by Fermi for the conversion of a stable into a radioactive isotope by neutron capture is sometimes known as the 'neutron activation' of an element. The availability of a very high flux of slow neutrons in certain designs of nuclear reactors (see Chapter 9) makes it relatively easy to produce large quantities of radioactive isotopes. The second method, now used on a fairly large scale, utilizes beams of positively charged particles (protons or deuterons) from a cyclotron—basically the same principle as used by Rutherford when he used alpha particles as projectiles to induce nuclear transmutations. The cyclotron method is used to advantage in order to produce:

(a) Radioactive isotopes of different properties from those particular isotopes which are available by neutron activation. An outstanding example is ^{22}Na $(t_{\frac{1}{2}} = 2\cdot6 \text{ y})$ which is more convenient for certain medical work (e.g. blood circulation tests) than the comparatively short-lived ^{24}Na $(t_{\frac{1}{2}} = 15 \text{ h})$. The longer-lived form of radioactive sodium is produced by deuteron bombardment of magnesium:

$$^{24}_{12}\text{Mg} + {}^{2}_{1}\text{H} \rightarrow {}^{22}_{11}\text{Na} + {}^{4}_{2}\text{He}$$

$$^{22}_{11}\text{Na} \; (t_{\frac{1}{2}} = 2\cdot6 \text{ y}) \rightarrow {}^{22}_{10}\text{Ne} + \beta^{+}$$

(b) Radioactive isotopes of high 'specific activity'. To explain this term we must revert to the process of neutron activation and note that in such a reaction as:

$$^{23}_{11}\text{Na} + {}^{1}_{0}\text{n} \rightarrow {}^{24}_{11}\text{Na}$$

only a small fraction of the sodium atoms are converted into the radioactive isotope. The radioactive sodium prepared in this way is therefore diluted with a great excess of normal sodium, $^{23}_{11}$Na. We shall see in Chapter 11 that this is a disadvantage in certain specialized uses of radioactive sodium. By contrast, the ^{22}Na prepared from magnesium by bombardment with deuterons is free from any inactive ^{23}Na, other than any traces of sodium which may be present as a trace impurity in the magnesium. The ^{22}Na is, of course, present in a large excess of unreacted magnesium, but this may readily be removed by chemical methods.

Similarly, cyclotron bombardment is used to prepare radioactive iron of high specific activity by the nuclear reaction:

$$^{55}_{25}\text{Mn} + {}^{2}_{1}\text{H} \rightarrow {}^{55}_{26}\text{Fe} + {}^{1}_{0}\text{n} + {}^{1}_{0}\text{n}$$

followed by chemical separation of iron from manganese. The same isotope could have been produced in a nuclear reactor by neutron activation:

$$^{54}_{26}\text{Fe} + {}^{1}_{0}\text{n} = {}^{55}_{26}\text{Fe}$$

but would then have been mixed with the stable isotopes of iron.

MATHEMATICAL TREATMENT OF NEUTRON ACTIVATION

The production of radioactive isotopes by neutron activation is now so important, both in pure and applied science, that it is necessary to study the mathematical treatment of this reaction, in order to be able to calculate the yield as a function of time, half-life, etc. The treatment in the following section is specifically related to neutron activation, but may easily be extended to cover the production of radioactive isotopes by cyclotron bombardment. The symbols used are as follows:

n = number of atoms of the target isotope;

f = slow neutron flux (neutrons cm^{-2} sec^{-1});

t = duration of bombardment (sec);

W = weight of target element present (g);

θ = fractional isotope abundance of the target isotope in the element as it occurs in nature;

$t_{\frac{1}{2}}$ = half-life of the radioactive isotope produced;

σ = neutron activation cross-section of the target isotope.

The symbol σ (cross-section) requires some explanation. The number of successful interactions of slow neutrons with the nuclei of the target isotope (successful, that is, in consummating an n, gamma reaction) will obviously be directly proportional to the factors n, f, t. Some additional factor or factors are required, to express the likelihood of reaction of a given neutron when it passes near a given nucleus. Involved in this factor will be the physical dimensions of the nucleus, and a dimensionless number or probability factor, representing the probability of a given collision being effective—for the fact of collision does not of itself guarantee success in a nuclear reaction, as the colliding bodies may separate again by elastic collision, or may undergo some side reaction. The total number of effective collisions = $n.\sigma.f.t.$ It may easily be checked, using dimensional analysis, that σ has the dimensions of area (cm^2), and this accounts for the slightly misleading phrase 'cross-section'. The usual units in which to express σ are 'barns' where 1 barn = 10^{-24} cm^2.

If we were simply considering the conversion of a stable isotope A to another stable isotope B by neutron activation, e.g. ${}^1_1H + {}^1_0n = {}^2_1H$ then the production of B could be expressed:

$$n_B = n_A\sigma.f.t.$$

provided that the total extent of the conversion is so small that the value of n_A remains approximately constant.

We are, however, interested in the case where the product B is radioactive, and will itself change to a third isotope, C.

It becomes necessary to set up a differential equation to express the situation:

$$\frac{dn_B}{dt} = n_A \cdot \sigma \cdot f - \lambda_B n_A \tag{8.1}$$

where λ_B is the radioactive rate constant for the nuclear reaction $B \to C$. The integration of equation 8.1 gives

$$n_B = \frac{n_A \cdot \sigma \cdot f}{\lambda_B} (1 - e^{-\lambda_B t})$$

assuming that $n_B = 0$ at $t = 0$, i.e. that we commence with pure A. We are usually concerned, not so much with the actual number of atoms, n_B, of the radioactive isotope as with the intensity of the radioactivity—the rate of radioactive decay of B to C. This may be expressed as $\lambda_B \cdot n_B$:

$$\lambda_B \cdot n_B = n_A \cdot \sigma \cdot f \cdot (1 - e^{-\lambda_B t}) \tag{8.2}$$

This equation enables us to calculate the amount of radioactivity due to B after any given duration of irradiation. The following practical hints may be useful in applying the equation:

(a) The calculation of the number of atoms, n_A, requires a knowledge of the isotopic abundance ratio, θ. It is simplest to use this as a *fraction*, e.g. the element chlorine occurs naturally as 75·5 per cent ^{35}Cl, 24·5 per cent ^{37}Cl. In considering the reaction: $^{37}Cl + {}_0^1n = {}^{38}Cl$ (a beta emitter of half-life 37 min) use $\theta = 0·245$.

We need, also, to use the weight (W g) of the element chlorine in the sample, the gramme atomic weight of chlorine (35·5) and the value of Avogadro's number, $6·02 \times 10^{23}$. For example, a sample which contains 1 g of chlorine will contain $1 \times 6·02 \times 10^{23}/35·5$ atoms of the element chlorine of which $0·245 \times 6·02 \times 10^{23}/35·5$ will be atoms of the particular isotope of mass 37.

(b) The bracketed expression in equation 8.2 is sometimes called the 'growth factor' (G). It may more conveniently be written as $(1 - e^{-0·693t/t_{\frac{1}{2}}})$. The units of t and $t_{\frac{1}{2}}$ respectively need not be restricted to seconds, as long as t is the *same* units as $t_{\frac{1}{2}}$. The form of the growth function is such that when t becomes much larger than $t_{\frac{1}{2}}$, that is when the activation is prolonged to several half-lives of the product, then the growth factor approaches unity, and the amount of radioactivity due to B is said to reach a 'saturation' value. This is due to the fact that as much B decays to C in each further interval of time as is produced by neutron activation from A. A further result of importance is that when $t = t_{\frac{1}{2}}$, the growth factor $= 0.5$. Other values of the growth factor are most easily calculated as follows:

$$G = 1 - \text{antilog}_{10}\left(-\frac{0.693}{2.303}\,t/t_{\frac{1}{2}}\right) = 1 - \text{antilog}_{10}\left(-0.301\,t/t_{\frac{1}{2}}\right)$$

When $t/t_{\frac{1}{2}}$ is less than 0.2, a simple approximation is given by:

$$G = 0.693\,t/t_{\frac{1}{2}}$$

(c) The equation 8.2 gives the amount of radioactivity present in the sample at the end of the irradiation. It will often be necessary to allow for the subsequent decay of this radioactivity once the sample is removed from the exposure to neutrons. The appropriate expression is:

$$A = A_0 \cdot e^{-0.693t\,/t_{\frac{1}{2}}} \tag{8.3}$$

where A_o is the rate of radioactive disintegration at the end of the irradiation and A_t is the rate of radioactive disintegration after interval t following the removal from exposure to neutrons.

The expression $e^{-0.693t/t_{\frac{1}{2}}}$, or decay factor (D), may be calculated:

$$D = \text{antilog}\left(-\frac{0.693}{2.303}\,t/t_{\frac{1}{2}}\right) = \text{antilog}\left(-0.301 \cdot t/t_{\frac{1}{2}}\right)$$

(d) The mathematical treatment which we have applied to the process of neutron activation employed certain assumptions which are normally justifiable but which require care in special cases. The assumptions are:

(i) The total number of atoms of the target isotope remains practically constant.

(ii) The neutron flux remains constant.

(iii) The extent of neutron capture by B is negligible.

(iv) Neutron capture by A leads only to B, i.e. we neglect side reactions such as those which result in the expulsion of a proton or an alpha particle, or in nuclear fission. It will be found that tables of nuclear cross-sections include the 'slow' neutron activation cross-sections as a separate list, in cases where competing reactions occur. In such cases the activation cross-section is, of course, less than the total cross-section for neutron capture by that particular isotope.

(e) Examples of the mathematical treatment are given below.

(i) A silver coin weighing 20 g is irradiated with a flux of 10^4 slow neutrons cm^{-2} sec^{-1}, from an antimony–beryllium neutron source for 5 min. At the end of a further 5 min following its removal from the neutron source, what will be the disintegration rate of ^{108}Ag? ($t_{\frac{1}{2}} = 2 \cdot 3$ min).

$$t = 5 \text{ min}$$

$$t/t_{\frac{1}{2}} = 5/2 \cdot 3 = 2 \cdot 17$$

Growth factor $G = 1 - \text{antilog}_{10}\,(-0 \cdot 301\ t/t_{\frac{1}{2}})$

$$= 1 - \text{antilog}_{10}\,(-0 \cdot 653)$$

$$= 1 - \text{antilog}_{10}\,(\bar{1} \cdot 347)$$

$$= 1 - 0 \cdot 222 = 0 \cdot 778$$

Decay factor $D = \text{antilog}_{10}\,(-0 \cdot 301\ t/t_{\frac{1}{2}})$

$$= \text{antilog}_{10}\,(\bar{1} \cdot 347) = 0 \cdot 222$$

The nuclear reaction in which we are interested is:

$$^{107}_{47}Ag + {}^{1}_{0}n \xrightarrow{(\sigma = 30 \text{ barns})} {}^{108}_{47}Ag$$

The isotope abundance of ^{107}Ag is 51 per cent.

The number of atoms of the isotope ^{107}Ag in the coin

$$= \frac{20}{107 \cdot 9} \times 6 \cdot 02 \times 10^{23} \times 0 \cdot 51$$

$$= 5 \cdot 69 \times 10^{22}$$

Substituting the above values in equations 8.2 and 8.3, we derive:

$$\lambda_B . n_B = n_a . \sigma . f . G . D$$

$$= 5 \cdot 69 \times 10^{22} \times 30 \times 10^{-24} \times 10^4 \times 0 \cdot 778 \times 0 \cdot 222$$

$$= 2 \cdot 95 \times 10^3 \text{ disintegrations sec}^{-1}$$

or $\qquad 1 \cdot 77 \times 10^5$ disintegrations min^{-1}

(ii) A sample which contains one μg $(10^{-6}$ g$)$ of arsenic is irradiated for 14 h in a nuclear reactor at a flux of 10^{12} slow neutrons cm^{-2} sec^{-1}. What is the disintegration rate due to the 26·7 h ^{76}As, immediately upon removal from the reactor?

$$t/t_{\frac{1}{2}} = 14/26\cdot7 = 0\cdot52$$

Growth factor $G = 1 - \text{antilog}\ (-0\cdot301 \times t/t_{\frac{1}{2}})$

$$= 1 - 0\cdot698 = 0\cdot302$$

Decay factor $D = 1$

The nuclear reaction is:

$$^{75}_{33}\text{As} + ^{1}_{0}\text{n} \xrightarrow{(\sigma = 4\cdot3 \text{ barns})} ^{76}_{33}\text{As}$$

The isotope abundance of ^{75}As is 100 per cent.

The number of atoms of ^{75}As in the sample is:

$$\frac{10^{-6}}{74\cdot9} \times 6\cdot02 \times 10^{23} \times 1\cdot00 = 8\cdot04 \times 10^{15}$$

Substituting the above values in equation 8·2 we derive:

$$\lambda_B \cdot n_B = 8\cdot04 \times 10^{15} \times 4\cdot3 \times 10^{-24} \times 10^{12} \times 0\cdot302 \times 1\cdot00$$

$$= 1\cdot04 \times 10^4 \text{ disintegrations sec}^{-1}$$

$$= 6\cdot24 \times 10^5 \text{ disintegrations min}^{-1}$$

9

NUCLEAR FISSION

The discovery of nuclear fission arose out of the work on artificial radioactivity which we discussed in the last chapter. The various elements 'activated' by Fermi included the elements uranium and thorium. These were, of course, radioactive even before the exposure to neutrons but the significant result was a large increase of beta radioactivity upon exposure to neutrons. The 'extra' beta activity which was present at the end of the activation showed a half-life of approximately 23 min (this happened, fortuitously, to be about the same for the uranium as for the thorium). By analogy with the general pattern of the neutron activation of the lighter elements, Fermi (1934) interpreted the nuclear reactions as follows:

$$^{238}_{92}U + ^{1}_{0}n \rightarrow ^{239}_{92}U$$

$$^{239}_{92}U \ (t_{\frac{1}{2}} = 23 \cdot 5 \ \text{min}) \rightarrow ^{239}_{93}X + \beta$$

$$^{232}_{90}Th + ^{1}_{0}n \rightarrow ^{233}_{90}Th$$

$$^{233}_{90}Th \ (t_{\frac{1}{2}} = 22 \ \text{min}) \rightarrow ^{233}_{91}Pa + \beta$$

The successive operations of neutron capture and beta decay should lead to the formation of an element, one higher in atomic number. In the case of thorium, this would lead to a new isotope of the previously known radioactive element, protactinium. In the case of uranium, the product would be X, a previously unknown element, of atomic number 93.

In fact, it appeared from Fermi's work that the isotope of mass 239 and atomic number 93 was itself radioactive, for even after allowing time for the uranium-239 to decay, the residual beta radioactivity in the sample was far higher than that due to the natural radioactivity of the uranium. Fermi postulated that a whole series of transuranium elements could arise by successive beta decay from the original product, $^{239}_{92}U$, of the neutron activation. $^{239}_{92}U \rightarrow ^{239}_{93}X \rightarrow ^{239}_{94}X' \rightarrow$ etc. Attempts were made from 1936 onwards to discover the chemical properties of these new elements, using the radiochemical methods which have been described in Chapter 6. Throughout the period 1934 to 1938, it was not recognized that nuclear fission had occurred in Fermi's sample of uranium, and that the fission products comprised a range of elements of medium atomic number from about 30 to 65. In several research papers, and in at least one university textbook on chemistry, published before 1939, the chemistry of the so-called transuranium elements was discussed in some detail, without recognizing that most of the radioactivity present was due to an entirely different group of elements, which we now know as the fission products. The true properties of the transuranium elements (neptunium, plutonium, americium, etc.) could only be discovered later (1940 and subsequently), when methods such as solvent extraction were developed, for separating them from the predominance of radio-activity due to the fission products.

The radiochemists who were engaged upon the study of the products of neutron activation of uranium included the Joliot-Curies at the Collège de Paris and Hahn at the Kaiser Wilhelm Institut in Berlin. As the political history of Europe moved through the events of the Abyssinian War, the Spanish Civil War and the Munich settlement to the outbreak of World War II, the secret of atomic fission awaited discovery in laboratories in Paris, Cambridge, Rome, Zurich and Berlin. Robert Jungk has written that, 'it is interesting to speculate what the consequences would have been if the chain reaction in uranium had been correctly interpreted in Rome in 1934 . . . . Would Mussolini and Hitler then have been the first to develop the atom bomb?'

Frau Ida Noddack, at Freiburg, who had personal experience of the discovery of a new element, rhenium (1924), was sceptical about Fermi's 'transuranium elements', and wrote in 1934, 'It would be conceivable that when heavy nuclei are bombarded with neutrons, the nuclei in question might break into a number of large pieces which would no doubt be isotopes of known elements but not neighbours of the elements subjected to radiation.'

Otto Hahn felt that Frau Noddack's suggestion of the bursting of the uranium nucleus was 'really absurd'—as indeed it was in the light of accepted physics—and until 1938 he interpreted his own results in terms of the supposed trans-uranium elements. However, a paper published in 1938 by Irène Joliot-Curie with Savitch as co-author mentioned certain anomalies: one of the products of the bombardment of uranium with neutrons persisted in behaving chemically like lanthanum. This particular product had previously been thought to be an isotope of actinium (atomic number 89) which could have come from the emission of two successive alpha particles from a transuranic element of atomic number 93. Hahn and Strassmann tried to repeat the work of

Joliot-Curie and Savitch, and were forced to conclude that the chemical facts could not all be fitted into the 'trans-uranium' theory. In their experiments, a beta active 'lanthanum' fraction, from neutron irradiated uranium, remained with added 'carrier' lanthanum despite successive fractional crystallization of lanthanum oxalate, whereas actinium (deliberately added as the beta active isotope Ac-228), remained in the mother liquor. Again, Hahn and Strassmann isolated another chemical fraction which appeared to contain barium, but it was still possible that an isotope of radium, rather than barium, was present, arising perhaps from the loss of three successive alpha particles from an element of atomic number 94. Hahn was an expert in the chemistry of radium, and he and Strassmann carefully checked this possible explanation. In one series of experiments they added barium chloride to a solution of the supposed trans-uranium elements, and converted the barium salt by addition of the appropriate chemical reagents into a series of different compounds which were isolated successfully by crystallization, and finally the barium was recovered again as the chloride and its radioactivity was measured using a Geiger counter. The 'specific activity' of the barium (expressed as disintegrations per min per unit weight) was found to remain at its original value after the complete chemical 'cycle':

Chloride—succinate—nitrate—carbonate—ferrimannite—chloride

Hahn and Strassmann were forced to write on December 22nd, 1938 in a scientific report which was published in the journal *Die Naturwissenschaften* dated January 6, 1939, words which may be somewhat freely translated: 'Our "radium isotopes" have the properties of barium: as chemists we ought really to say that in the new substances we are not dealing with radium but with barium.' Later in the same paper they express their dilemma in these words: 'We ought as chemists to revise the [former] scheme . . . and instead of Ra, Ac, Th to write the symbols Ba, La, Ce. As "nuclear chemists," closely concerned with physics, we are not yet able to resolve this anomaly, which contradicts all previous experience in nuclear physics. It is possible that our results arise from a series of coincidences.' Robert Jungk writes that he was told by Otto Hahn himself, twenty years later, 'After the manuscript had been mailed, the whole thing once more seemed so improbable to me that I wished I could get the document back out of the mail box.'

A copy of this paper came privately from Hahn to his former colleague, Fraulein Meitner, then a refugee in Denmark from Hitler's racial laws. Her nephew, the nuclear physicist O. R. Frisch, was also a refugee, at the Institute of Theoretical Physics, Copenhagen. During the Christmas holidays at Kungelv near Göteborg they discussed the possible mechanism of the break-up of a uranium nucleus into lighter fragments which included barium.

Niels Bohr, the Director of the Institute of Theoretical Physics, Copenhagen, had already published (in 1936) a 'liquid drop' theory of nuclear reactions. The protons and neutrons within the nucleus are so closely packed that it shows some of the properties of a liquid phase. When the nucleus is bombarded by an alpha particle, proton or neutron, etc., the incoming particle is first captured to form a very short-lived 'compound nucleus'. The extra energy introduced by the incoming particle (as kinetic energy plus binding energy) becomes rapidly shared out amongst all the particles within the nucleus, and the surface of the 'liquid drop' increases its irregular motions until a particle breaks away. Usually the outcoming fragment is either identical with the incoming particle or is of a comparable size—certainly no larger than an alpha particle. The random movements of the closely packed particles within the nucleus could give rise to quite large distortions of the 'liquid drop', but they are constrained by cohesive forces at the nuclear surface, analogous to surface tension in the case of a liquid.

Frisch and Meitner came to realize that for a large nucleus like that of uranium, the surface forces are insufficient to restrain the distorsions if the drop suffers elongation, formation of a waist and finally separation of the two halves. The final stage in such a process would be assisted by the coulombic repulsion of the like charges on either half.

In this way they arrived at the concept of nuclear 'fission' (the word 'fission' was borrowed from the process of cell-division in biology). The scientific journal *Nature*, published in London, included in its issue of 11 February 1939, a letter from Frisch and Meitner, on the 'Disintegration of uranium by neutrons: a new type of nuclear reaction.' Their paper set the nuclear physicists in half a dozen different countries into a flurry of experimentation and publication of their results. About one hundred papers were published on the subject of nuclear fission during 1939.

The excitement about this new discovery of nuclear fission was based upon two scientific factors: (1) energy release, (2) neutron release.

ENERGY RELEASE

Further experiments soon showed that large amounts of energy were released in the process of fission—for example the fission fragments moved apart at high speeds. This would be expected due to the electrostatic repulsion of highly charged nuclei. The release of energy was shown to be a theoretical consequence of the fact that the total mass, say of fragments of nominal mass numbers 95 and 139 respectively, together with that of one excess neutron is less than that of uranium of mass number 235. It was previously known that the Law of Conservation of Mass does not apply rigidly to atomic events, but that we still retain a Law of Conservation of Energy provided that we regard mass as having an intrinsic energy given by the equation:

$$E = mc^2 \text{ (Einstein, 1905)}$$

where E is the intrinsic energy of a particle of mass, m, and c is the velocity of light.

The Einstein equation may be used to calculate that one mass unit (on the scale for which oxygen isotope-16 weighs 16·000 units) is equivalent to 931 MeV. Changes of a small fraction of one mass unit must occur in many nuclear reactions, because it is found experimentally, using mass spectrometry to measure the masses of individual isotopes very accurately, that these masses are not whole numbers and that the deviation from the nearest whole number (the 'mass defect') changes throughout the Periodic Table. This was expressed in a striking form in 1927 by F. W. Aston, an expert in the field of mass spectrometry, who expressed the deviations as a 'packing fraction', equal to

$$\frac{\text{Isotopic weight} - \text{Mass number}}{\text{Mass number}} \times 10,000$$

where the mass number is the nearest whole number to the isotopic weight. Some examples are shown in Table 9.1.

Table 9.1. Examples of Packing Fractions

Isotope	Isotopic mass	Mass number	Packing fraction
$_{1}^{1}\text{H}$	1·00814	1	+81·4
$_{3}^{7}\text{Li}$	7·01823	7	+26
$_{42}^{95}\text{Mo}$	94·9357	95	−6·8
$_{92}^{235}\text{U}$	235·117	235	+5·0

The general trend of the variation in packing fraction with mass number is shown in *Figure 9.1*. One would expect a large release of energy in any nuclear reaction in which the products have lower packing fractions than the reactants, since mass is lost during the reaction. The packing fraction diagram is a convenient qualitative means of summarizing the mass spectrometric data. In working out practical calculations for particular nuclear reactions, it is

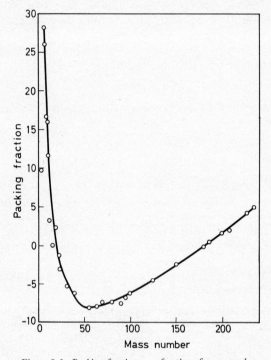

Figure 9.1. Packing fraction as a function of mass number

better to work directly with the values of the isotopic masses. For example, the nuclear reaction between lithium and a proton,

$$_3^7\text{Li} + {}_1^1\text{H} \rightarrow {}_2^4\text{He} + {}_2^4\text{He}$$

is accompanied by a loss of mass which appears as kinetic energy of the products of the reaction:

Total mass of reactants = 7·0182 + 1·0081 = 8·0263 units

Total mass of products = 2 × 4·00387   = 8·0077 units

Loss of mass = 0·0186 units

106

The gain in energy corresponding to 0·0186 mass units may be calculated as follows:

$$m = 0\cdot0186 \text{ mass units} = 3\cdot10 \times 10^{-26} \text{ g}$$
$$c = 3 \times 10^{10} \text{ cm sec}^{-1} \text{ (velocity of light)}$$
$$E = mc^2 = 3\cdot10 \times 10^{-26} \times (3 \times 10^{10})^2 \text{ ergs}$$
$$= 27\cdot9 \times 10^{-6} \text{ ergs}$$
$$= 17\cdot4 \text{ MeV}$$

This kinetic energy is divided between two alpha particles, each of energy 8·7 MeV. Experimentally, the energy of the ejected alpha particles were determined as approximately 8·5 MeV. (The kinetic energy of the incident proton may be neglected in the above calculation as it is only 0·07 MeV.)

A similar mass and energy balance may be drawn up for the fission of the uranium isotope, U-235 by a neutron to produce two neutrons and two fragments, which after a succession of beta dis-integrations arrive at the stable isotopes, Mo-95 and La-139.

$$^{235}_{92}U + {}^1_0n \rightarrow {}^{95}_{42}Mo + {}^{139}_{57}La + 2{}^1_0n + 7\beta$$

Total mass of reactants $= 235\cdot117 + 1\cdot009 = 236\cdot126$

Total mass of products $= 94\cdot9357 + 138\cdot950 + 2(1\cdot009)$
$$= 235\cdot904$$

Loss of mass $= 236\cdot126 - 235\cdot904 = 0\cdot222$

The calculation for lithium has already shown that a loss of 0·0186 mass units is equivalent to an energy release of 17·4 MeV. By simple proportion a loss of 0·222 mass units is equivalent to an energy release of

$$17\cdot4 \times \frac{0\cdot222}{0\cdot0186} = 207 \text{ MeV}$$

The exact value of the energy release varies somewhat according to the mass number of the fission fragments. Experimentally, the average energy release has been estimated as 205 MeV, distributed as follows:

Kinetic energy of fission fragments =	165 MeV
Energy released in radioactive decay of fragments =	16·2 MeV
Energy released as kinetic energy of neutrons =	5 MeV
Energy released instantaneously as gamma rays =	7·8 MeV
Neutrino energy associated with β-decay =	11 MeV
Total =	205 MeV

NEUTRON RELEASE

The considerations given above would have sufficed to establish the phenomenon of nuclear fission as worthy of intensive research and theoretical study. The second factor that gave the subject a potential industrial and even military significance was one that was not immediately obvious from Frisch and Meitner's paper of 11 February 1939—the fact that neutrons were liberated as a result

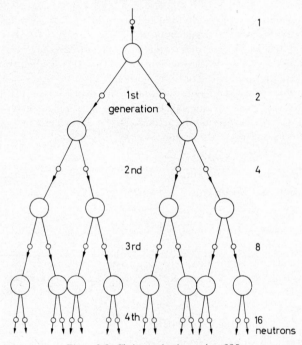

Figure 9.2. Chain reaction in uranium-235

of nuclear fission. If more than one neutron were liberated a 'chain reaction' would be theoretically possible (*Figure 9.2*). The multiplication of neutrons as a result of fission was established experimentally in Paris by H. von Halban, F. Joliot and L. Kowarski and reported in *Nature*, 18 March 1939.

Sufficient basic scientific knowledge had been openly published by the outbreak of the World War II to indicate that it might be possible to harness the energy released in the fission of uranium (*a*) to supply heat and a large and sustained flux of neutrons by a controlled chain reaction, (b) to make explosions by a rapid chain reaction.

The development of the graphite moderated uranium pile and of the atomic bomb then followed in the United States between 1940 and 1944, with the collaboration of British, French and Canadian teams.

It will now be necessary to abandon the purely historical sequence and to review the main physical and chemical facts that have come to light since 1939, and which bear upon the phenomenon of nuclear fission and upon its practical application.

BASIC PHYSICS OF NUCLEAR FISSION

NEUTRON PHYSICS

The neutrons which are released during the fission of uranium travel at high speeds, with a kinetic energy of up to 20 MeV. Not all the neutrons have this maximum energy, and an average

Table 9.2. Numbers of Successive Elastic Collisions Necessary to Reduce Neutron Energy from 2 MeV to 0·025 eV

Isotope	Hydrogen-1	Deuterium	Beryllium-9	Carbon-12
Numbers of collisions	18	25	90	114

value of 2 MeV is commonly quoted. Such neutrons are called 'fast neutrons'.

The kinetic energy of neutrons may be reduced by collisions with atoms of uranium or with materials such as hydrogen, deuterium or carbon which are introduced as 'moderators'. The collisions to which we refer are not those which lead to neutron capture, as in hydrogen or uranium. Neutrons may collide with a nucleus without leading to fission or to capture. Such collisions are called either 'elastic' or 'inelastic collision'.

Elastic collisions occur when the kinetic energy of the neutron before collision is shared between the colliding nucleus and the on-going neutron. The laws of conservation of energy and of momentum apply to such collisions, and it may be shown that the neutrons will lose an amount of energy which depends upon the mass of the colliding nucleus. Collision with light nuclei such as hydrogen (Table 9.2) are more effective in reducing the neutron energy than elastic collisions with heavy nuclei such as uranium.

Inelastic collisions occur when the kinetic energy of the neutron is partly converted into nuclear energy in the colliding nucleus. This process leaves us with an energetically excited state of the target nucleus (which eventually re-emits the excess energy as a gamma ray), plus a neutron of lower energy. It turns out that this process is more important than 'elastic collision' for heavy nuclei such as uranium. The loss of energy by the neutron is relatively large, e.g. a single inelastic collision with the nucleus of uranium-238 removes about 0·6 MeV from a 2 MeV neutron.

The speed of a 'fast neutron' may be reduced by a succession of 'elastic' and/or 'inelastic' collisions until it is travelling no faster than the speed of any free particle, at the temperature of its surroundings. The kinetic theory of gases predicts that such particles will have a range of speeds, such that the energy corresponding to the most probable velocity is kT, where k is the Boltzmann constant, $= 0.86 \times 10^{-5}$ eV per degree, and T is the absolute temperature. At 20° C, $kT = 0.86 \times 10^{-5} \times 293$ eV $= 0.025$ eV (which corresponds to a speed of about 2,200 m/sec).

Neutrons which have been slowed to the range of energies defined above are called 'thermal neutrons'. They still continue to move about the medium in which they are contained, until they are either captured or escape from the system. The motion of thermal neutrons in nuclear reactors and other systems is studied by physicists and engineers and is known as 'neutron diffusion'.

When 'fast neutrons' are being slowed down to become 'thermal neutrons', the values of their energies must pass through an intermediate region. The region 1 to 100 eV is particularly important (see the following section) and such neutrons are often called 'epithermal neutrons'.

FISSION AND CAPTURE CROSS-SECTIONS

The interactions of neutrons with uranium can involve several different processes. We have to distinguish between neutrons of different kinetic energies and between the two main isotopes of uranium, of mass 235 and 238 respectively.

Uranium-238

Uranium-238 undergoes fission only when bombarded with neutrons of energies above 1·0 MeV. From 2 to 6 MeV the fission cross-section is about 0·58 barns. Thermal neutrons (0·025 eV) will not cause the fission of this isotope. Thermal neutrons and neutrons of intermediate energy have a finite probability of capture to yield U-239. This isotope decays with a half-life of 23·5 min and the emission of a beta particle, producing element 93 (neptunium) which in turn decays to element 94 (plutonium) which is a moderately long-lived alpha emitter:

$$^{238}_{92}\text{U} + ^{1}_{0}\text{n} \rightarrow ^{239}_{92}\text{U} \xrightarrow[\text{min}, \beta^-]{23\cdot5} ^{239}_{93}\text{Np} \xrightarrow[\text{days}, \beta^-]{2\cdot33} ^{239}_{94}\text{Pu}$$

$$^{239}_{94}\text{Pu} \xrightarrow[\text{years}]{24,300} ^{235}_{92}\text{U} + ^{4}_{2}\text{He}$$

The chemistry of the transuranium elements, neptunium, plutonium, etc., is discussed in Chapter 10.

This process of neutron capture by an (*n*, gamma) reaction is always present, even in the case of those isotopes which are susceptible to *fission* by thermal neutrons, as shown by the examples given in Table 9.3.

Table 9.3. Fission and Capture Cross-sections*

Isotope	Cross-section for fission (barns)	Cross-section for neutron capture	Product of neutron capture	
$^{235}_{92}\text{U}$	582	112	$^{236}_{92}\text{U}$	alpha $2\cdot4 \times 10^7$ y
$^{233}_{92}\text{U}$	527	52	$^{234}_{92}\text{U}$	alpha $2\cdot5 \times 10^5$ y
$^{239}_{94}\text{Pu}$	746	315	$^{240}_{94}\text{Pu}$	alpha 6,600 y
$^{241}_{94}\text{Pu}$	1025	390	$^{242}_{94}\text{Pu}$	alpha $3\cdot7 \times 10^5$ y

* Data from: D. J. Hughes and R. B. Schwartz, *Neutron Cross-sections*, Brookhaven National Laboratory, U.S.A., BNL 325, 1958.

The physical aspects of the capture of neutrons by uranium-238 are important. The cross-section for this nuclear reaction has been measured using neutrons of closely controlled velocities (*Figure 9.3*). The graph shows 'resonance peaks' in the region of 6·6, 21·0, 36·5, 65 and 100 eV. In this respect, uranium is similar to many elements which undergo (*n*, γ) reactions, and which show one or more resonance peaks between 0·1 and 100 eV superimposed upon a general decrease of capture cross-section with increasing velocity. These features may be explained:

(*a*) *Decreasing cross-section* is proportional to the reciprocal of the neutron velocity, since the probability of interaction between the neutron and the nucleus, as measured by the cross-section, is proportional to the time the former spends in the vicinity of the latter.

(*b*) *Resonance absorption* is explained as being due to the neutron supplying just the right amount of kinetic energy to provide a transition from a lower to a higher energy level in the compound nucleus, these energy levels being separated by a few electron-volts, according to calculations by Niels Bohr.

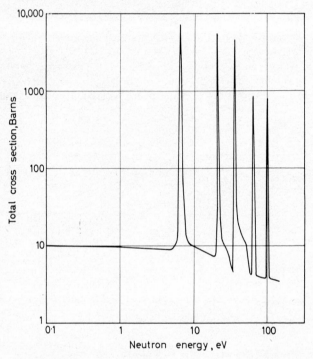

Figure 9.3. Cross-section of uranium-238 as a function of neutron energy
(Data from: Hughes and Schwartz, *Neutron Cross Sections*, BNL 325, 1958)

Uranium-235

This isotope is present as a minor constituent of normal uranium (1 atom out of every 139) but it is responsible for most of the fission events which occur when uranium is bombarded with 'thermal' neutrons. The isotopic fission cross-section is about 582 barns for 0·025 eV neutrons, so that the effective fission cross-section for the normal mixture of 235 and 238 is about 582/139 or 4·2 barns. The fission cross-section for 2 MeV neutrons is of the same order for the 235 as for the 238 isotope—and in fact for most of the heavier elements (Table 9.4). The high cross-section for fission by 'thermal'

112

neutrons is a selective feature of certain types of heavy nuclei e.g. $^{235}_{92}$U, $^{233}_{92}$U, $^{239}_{94}$Pu (Table 9.4). These are all isotopes of *even* atomic number but *odd* mass number, i.e. with an even number of protons and an odd number of neutrons (an 'even–odd' nucleus).

Table 9.4. Fission Cross-sections of Heavy Isotopes

Isotope	Cross-section (Barns)	
	at 0·025 eV	*at* 2 MeV
Thorium-232	< 0·0002	0·11
Uranium-233	527	2·0
Uranium-235	582	1·3
Uranium-238	< 0·0005	0·58
Plutonium-239	746	2·1

SPONTANEOUS FISSION

Using an approximate theory of nuclear stability, Bohr and Wheeler estimated that a hypothetical isotope of atomic number 120 and mass number 320 would spontaneously undergo nuclear fission.

This instability would largely be due to the mutual repulsion of the protons. By classical physics, an isotope should either be too unstable to exist—like the hypothetical $^{320}_{120}$(?)—or it should not suffer spontaneous fission. The fission of the known heavy isotopes, such as those of uranium, should only be possible as the result of the addition of external energy; for example, the binding energy and kinetic energy of a neutron. We may express this fact in another way by saying that the nucleus of any one of these heavy isotopes has insufficient internal energy to reach the critical energy required for fission: there exists a 'potential energy barrier'. This is equally true if we are talking not about fission but about the expulsion of an alpha particle, though the energy deficit is not the *same* for alpha decay as for fission. Wave mechanics show (see Chapter 7, p. 84) that there is a definite if small probability that an alpha particle will be found outside the nucleus even though the initial energy is less than the critical value. This also holds true for the emission of two fission fragments, but it turns out theoretically that the probability is even lower than that for alpha decay. The probability of alpha decay or of spontaneous fission is related to the respective 'half-lives' for these processes. A low probability means a long half-life. Examples are known of heavy isotopes which exhibit *both* alpha decay and spontaneous fission, the half-life for the latter process being much the longer.

Table 9.5. Half-lives for Spontaneous Fission

Isotope	Half-life for fission	Half-life for alpha decay
$^{238}_{92}U$	$8 \cdot 0 \times 10^{15}$ y	$4 \cdot 51 \times 10^9$ y
$^{235}_{92}U$	$1 \cdot 9 \times 10^{17}$	$7 \cdot 1 \times 10^8$ y
$^{238}_{92}Pu$	$3 \cdot 8 \times 10^{10}$ y	89·6 y
$^{240}_{94}Pu$	$1 \cdot 2 \times 10^{11}$	6600 y
$^{240}_{96}Cm$	$7 \cdot 9 \times 10^5$ y	26·8 d

The first example of spontaneous fission was that of *uranium-238*, discovered by the Russian physicists G. N. Flerov and K. A. Petrjak in 1940. Other examples are given in Table 9.5.

THE PRODUCTS OF FISSION

We have so far considered the phenomena leading up to the act of nuclear fission in various heavy isotopes of uranium and other elements. The products of fission must now be considered in more detail.

For the purposes of the calculation of the energy released in fission (p. 107), we assumed that the compound nucleus of U-236 broke down into two fragments of mass numbers 95 and 139, with the emission also of two neutrons. We now need to consider (*a*) the emission of neutrons, and (*b*) the distribution of mass and atomic number amongst the fission products.

The Emission of Neutrons

The average number of neutrons released during the fission by slow neutrons of various isotopes is shown in Table 9.6.

Theoretically the compound nucleus of uranium-236 might split to give say $^{140}_{54}Xe$ and $^{96}_{38}Sr$, with no emission of neutrons. Both these isotopes would be highly unstable, however, for they contain an abnormally high excess of neutrons over protons. They could decay to more stable isotopes in two ways:

(*a*) By emission of successive beta particles, i.e. the mass number remains the same, but the atomic number increases:

$$^{140}_{54}Xe \rightarrow {}^{140}_{55}Cs \rightarrow {}^{140}_{56}Ba \rightarrow {}^{140}_{57}La \rightarrow {}^{140}_{58}Ce(stable)$$

(*b*) By emission of successive neutrons:

$$^{140}_{54}Xe \rightarrow {}^{139}Xe \rightarrow {}^{138}Xe \rightarrow {}^{137}Xe \rightarrow {}^{136}Xe \text{ (stable)}$$

Both these processes in fact occur, and the final products of the fission process consist of stable isotopes of atomic numbers between 30 and 66, neutrons and beta particles, e.g.

$$^{235}_{92}\text{U} + ^1_0\text{n} \rightarrow ^{95}_{42}\text{Mo} + ^{139}_{57}\text{La} + 2\,^1_0\text{n} + 7\beta$$

Neither the neutrons nor the beta particles are all emitted instantaneously. The beta particles are regulated, of course, by the

Table 9.6. Average Number of Neutrons Emitted per Thermal Fission*

Isotope	ν (thermal)	η	
		(thermal)	(fast)
^{233}U	2·51	2·28	2·4
^{235}U	2·47	2·07	2·3
^{239}Pu	2·90	2·10	2·6

Note: ν = neutrons released per fission.
η = neutrons released per neutron absorbed.
* Data from: J. F. Hill, Textbook of Reactor Physics, London, George Allen and Unwin, 1961.

Table 9.7. Delayed Neutrons in Fission of Uranium-235*

Half-life (sec)	Yield ($\times$ 0·64 %)	Energy (MeV)
55·7	0·033	0·25
22·7	0·219	0·46
6·2	0·196	0·40
2·3	0·395	0·45
0·61	0·115	0·42
0·23	0·042	—
	1·000	

* Data from: Reactor Physics Constants, ANL-5800, 1958.

half-lives of the successive members of the chain of radioactive fission products, which vary from seconds to years. The neutrons are emitted within 10^{-14} sec of the fission, except for a small fraction (about 0·6 per cent) which show some delay, and this property turns out to have considerable technological significance in the control of nuclear reactors. The 'delayed neutrons' fall into groups of characteristic half-life (Table 9.7).

It is probable that the 55·7 sec activity, for example, is due to the following chain of nuclear processes:

$$\text{Fission} \rightarrow {}^{87}_{35}\text{Br} \xrightarrow[t_{\frac{1}{2}}=55\cdot7\text{ sec}]{\beta\text{ decay}} {}^{87}_{36}\text{Kr} \xrightarrow[\text{a neutron}]{\text{emission of}} {}^{86}_{36}\text{Kr (stable)}$$

THE DISTRIBUTION OF ATOMIC NUMBER AND MASS NUMBER

The primary act of fission is rarely symmetrical as in

$$^{235}_{92}\text{U} + {}^{1}_{0}\text{n} \rightarrow 2^{117}_{46}\text{Pd} + 2^{1}_{0}\text{n}$$

where $^{117}_{46}\text{Pd}$ is an unstable isotope, decaying by one or more routes involving neutron and beta particle emission. It is usual to find

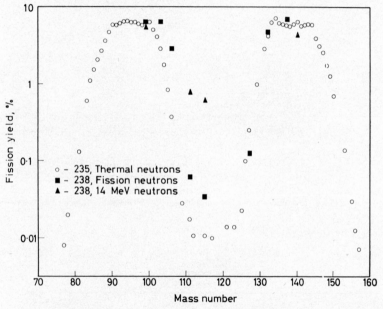

Figure 9.4. Yields of different masses by fission of uranium
[Data after: Steinberg and Glendenin (1955); Cuninghame (1957)]

that each individual fission produces a slightly different result, so that the results have to be expressed in terms of percentage yields (*Figure 9.4*). It is, of course, difficult to determine the nature of the primary products, for the experimental measurements have to be made upon the secondary products of partial or complete decay. The distribution of mass numbers shown in *Figure 9.4* has been determined by measuring the cumulative yields of stable or rela-

116

tively long-lived products, and will be identical with the primary distribution, except for the very slight perturbation caused by the short-lived neutron emitters. The primary distribution of atomic numbers is less easy to determine. One can approach this problem by measuring the independent fission yields of early members of the beta decay chain. These isotopes are usually very short-lived, and it is difficult to carry out the necessary chemical separations before they decay.

The data are best explained by the hypothesis of Glendenin, Coryell and Edwards (1946) of 'equal charge displacement'. Consider the fission of uranium-235. The 'compound nucleus' minus the fission neutrons weighs about 233·5 units. Suppose this divides to give fission fragments of mass approximately 139 and 95. The stable isotopes of atomic number 57 (La) and 42 (Mo) can be reached by beta decay chains. Total beta emission to reach stability $= (57 + 42) - 92 = 7$. This is shared equally between the heavy and the light chain, that is 3·5 beta to each. The most probable primary fission products will have $Z = 57 - 3$ or 4 ($_{53}^{139}I$ or $_{54}^{139}Xe$) and $Z = 42 - 3$ or 4 ($_{39}^{95}Y$ or $_{38}^{95}Sr$).

The mass distribution curve becomes more symmetrical as the energy of the incident particle increases (*Figure 9.4*). Qualitatively these results may be understood by considering the collective model of the nucleus (Chapter 7, p. 83). The irregular pulsations of the 'liquid' outer shell may lead to 'breaking away' of the fragments. The more rigid inner shells resist fragmentation, but are incorporated into one of the fragments of the outer layers. For example, consider an inner core of $A = 44$, and outer shells which total 190. The outer shells suffer symmetrical fission, $95 + 95$. One of the fragments is retained by the inner core to give $44 + 95 = 139$. The net result appears to be asymmetric, $95 + 139$. A more likely inner core is $_{20}^{40}Ca$ or $_{28}^{56}Ni$ (Hill, 1955) as these are rather stable nuclei. When fission is brought about by highly energetic particles, the inner core is included in the primary fragmentation and symmetrical fission occurs.

APPLICATIONS OF NUCLEAR FISSION

We have already referred to two of the outstanding features of nuclear fission, features which were already evident from the scientific papers published from several countries during 1939. Nuclear fission releases large amounts of energy, and at the same time releases neutrons which could potentially give rise to a chain reaction. The energy released in each fission of uranium-235 is about 200 MeV or $200 \times 3·56 \times 10^{-11}$ cal. If all the nuclei in 1 g at. wt. of the separated isotope uranium-235 could undergo fission, the total energy release would be $200 \times 3{\cdot}56 \times 10^{-11} \times 6{\cdot}02 \times 10^{23}/10^3$ kcal per g atom or $4{\cdot}3 \times 10^{12}$ kcal per g atom. This may be compared with the chemical energy of the order of 30 kcal per g atom (4 eV per carbon atom) which is released upon the combustion of coal or oil fuels.

THE FIRST SELF-SUSTAINING REACTOR

A self-sustaining nuclear chain reaction was first achieved at the University of Chicago on 2 December 1942 by a large team of scientists which included E. Fermi, then a refugee from Mussolini's Fascist regime. A description of the Chicago experiment in some

Table 9.8. A Neutron Balance Sheet*

	1000 thermal neutrons are captured within a fuel element
	94 absorbed in $^{235}U \rightarrow {}^{236}U$
	357 absorbed in $^{238}U \rightarrow {}^{239}Pu$
Leaves	549 absorbed by ^{235}U by fission
Produces	1314 fast neutrons + gain of 34 due to fast fission of ^{238}U
	1348 fast neutrons enter moderator
	23 escape from the core of the reactor
	142 suffer resonance capture by $^{238}U \rightarrow {}^{234}Pu$
Leaves	1183 slowed to thermal energies and diffuse throughout the moderator
	133 absorbed in moderator, structural materials, etc.
	50 escape from the core
Leaves	1000 to complete the cycle

* Data from: J. K. Dawson and G. Long, *Chemistry of Nuclear Power*, London, Newnes, 1959.

detail will reveal the many uncertainties which had to be investigated during the years 1939–42. It is not sufficient that, say, two neutrons are released per fission of uranium-235—it would be naive to suppose that a chain reaction is immediately possible along the lines 1, 2, 4, 8, 16, 32, 64, 128 fissions in succeeding 'generations'. It is necessary first to attempt to arrange that at least one neutron released by fission is eventually led to cause fission of a further nucleus rather than to escape from the apparatus, or become captured by uranium-235 to give uranium-236, by uranium-238 to uranium-239, or by other isotopes which are present as constructional materials or as impurities. The 'neutron multiplication factor' is the average number of neutrons produced per fission which are subsequently used to produce further fission, and this factor is usually represented by the symbol k. Table 9.8 shows the typical neutron balance for a thermal reactor fuelled by natural uranium, in a hypothetical design for which $k = 1{\cdot}000$.

The value of k is dependent upon the total amount of uranium in the reactor, the geometrical distribution of uranium within the moderator, and the extent of neutron losses due to capture by atoms of the moderator, by the engineering materials used in the construction of components (e.g. the cans in which the uranium fuel is contained), and by impurities, especially by traces of elements which have isotopes of very high capture cross-section, e.g. cadmium ($\sigma = 3{,}300$ barns), boron ($\sigma = 7{,}550$ barns) and samarium ($\sigma = 10{,}000$ barns).

It is not possible to achieve a self-sustaining nuclear chain reaction in pure natural uranium. If fission is started within a small piece of uranium, most of the fission neutrons escape from the surface of the sample. This could be prevented by using a very large sphere of natural uranium, where surface losses would be negligible compared with the possible total number of neutrons in the sphere. However, the chain reaction in an infinite mass of natural uranium is prevented because of three factors:

(*a*) The fission cross-sections for fast neutrons are relatively low for uranium-235 and uranium-238 (about 1·3 barns and 0·58 barns respectively at 2 MeV);

(*b*) The fission cross-section for uranium-238 decreases very sharply below 1·4 MeV;

(*c*) Fission neutrons of average energy 2 MeV will be rapidly reduced to below 1·4 MeV in natural uranium, because of the relatively high inelastic scattering cross-section of uranium-238 (2·47 barns). The loss of neutron energy in a single inelastic collision is usually more than 0·6 MeV.

One or two 'inelastic collisions' will reduce the neutron energy below the critical value for the fission of uranium-238, but the fission of 235 is still possible. However, many neutrons will continue to lose energy in very small steps as a result of 'elastic collision' with uranium nuclei (see p. 109). Eventually, a high proportion of these 'moderated' neutrons will be captured by uranium-238 at energies corresponding to the 'resonance peaks' at 6·6, 21·0, 36·5, 65 and 100 eV (*Figure 9.3*). Capture of neutrons in this way is often called the 'resonance trap', and it represents a barrier to the success of a fission chain reaction.

A chain reaction can only be sustained in natural uranium if the fission neutrons are deliberately slowed down to thermal levels by mixing the uranium with a 'moderator', such as graphite or heavy water.

Early experiments at Columbia University to measure k used a lattice structure of graphite with 7 tons of uranium oxide in iron containers. Fermi and Wigner had calculated that a matrix structure with separated lumps or bars of uranium oxide or metal had advantage over a uniform dispersion of uranium in graphite. The fission neutrons can be slowed down *below* the resonance levels during their transit from one bar of uranium to another, with less danger of encountering a nucleus of uranium-238 and being lost by resonance capture. Additionally, any resonance capture which does take place by a neutron entering a bar of uranium will usually take place near the surface—the bulk of the uranium in the interior is then said to be protected by 'self-shielding'.

The Columbia experiment was known to be too small to give a sustained chain reaction, but values of k could nevertheless be obtained, using a radium–beryllium mixture as a source of neutrons, placed at the centre of the assembly. It is possible to allow for the escape of neutrons from the outer surface of the graphite lattice, and to calculate a value for k_∞, the multiplication factor which would be expected for an infinitely large assembly. Even so, the value of k_∞ obtained by E. Fermi and others at Columbia towards the end of 1941 was only 0·87.

In order to achieve a larger value for k, much purer graphite and uranium was necessary than had been available for the Columbia experiments, e.g. the uranium oxide contained 2 to 5 per cent of impurities, and amongst the impurities in the graphite was 2 parts of boron per million parts of graphite. (This latter impurity is sufficient to increase by 50 per cent the loss of neutrons by capture in the graphite.) The production of high-grade graphite and uranium in tonnage quantities required new techniques in chemical engineering, analytical chemistry and metallurgy—and these branches of applied science have continued to be of major importance in the nuclear energy industry.

Using the purer materials, an exponential experiment in July 1942 was used to calculate a value of k_∞ for an infinite assembly of 1·07.

The full-scale thermal reactor which was eventually erected at Chicago (*Figure 9.5*) contained 6 tons of uranium metal and 50 tons of uranium oxide, and the graphite lattice was an incomplete sphere, about 25 ft. in diameter, containing 400 tons of graphite. The highest value of the multiplication factor was 1·0006, and the chain reaction (achieved for the first time on 2 December 1942) was controlled at a steady level corresponding to a power of 0·5 to 200 W by the partial insertion into the lattice of strips of cadmium metal (neutron absorption cross-section = 3,300 barns). The changes in reactivity of the nuclear reactor upon the insertion or withdrawal of the control strips would be instantaneous—making the reactor difficult to control—were it not for the 0·6 per cent of delayed neutrons which are emitted in fission (p. 115). Assume $k = 1·0006$. The mean life of prompt neutrons in such a reactor is about 1 msec, and hence if all neutrons were prompt the reactor power would increase by 0·06 per cent/msec or by $(1·0006)^{60,000}$, i.e. 160,000 times in 1 min. However, since 0·6 per cent of the neutrons are delayed with an average life of about 10 sec (Table 9.7) the overall average neutron life is about $0·006 \times 10 = 0·06$ sec.

Thus the reactor power would actually increase by 0·06 per cent in 0·06 sec or by $(1·0006)^{1000}$, i.e. 1·8 times in 1 min. In practice,

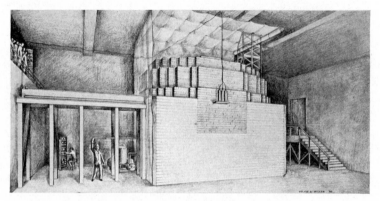

Figure 9.5. The first self-sustaining nuclear reactor
(By courtesy of the Argonne National Laboratory, U.S.A.)

reactors normally operate with values of k more nearly equal to one and power variations are much more sluggish, except when the reactor is being started up or shut down. Thus the person who controls the reactor would have ample time to correct any slight inaccuracies in the setting of the cadmium strips, before the reactor went completely out of control.

We will now look briefly at developments in nuclear reactor technology since 1942.

THERMAL REACTORS

Natural uranium reactors with graphite as a moderator are used by the British Central Electricity Generating Board in their nuclear power stations which started to come into commission in 1962 (*Figure 9.6*). The power levels are over a million times that of the Chicago reactor (Table 9.9).

121

The higher power levels bring important technological problems which were negligible in the case of the Chicago reactor.

(1) The prompt gamma rays emitted in fission and the gamma rays emitted during decay of the radioactive fission products would pose a great hazard to the health of the operators, if the reactor were not encased in a massive 'biological shield' of concrete. For example, at Calder Hall, Cumberland, each of the reactors with its shield weighed 33,000 tons.

(2) The heat evolved in the reactor must be removed by an elaborate system, otherwise the uranium and the graphite would

Table 9.9. Design Data for C.E.G.B. Nuclear Power Stations*

Location	Expected heat output per reactor (MW)	Notes
Bradwell (Essex) Each station has two reactors of the given specification.	530	236 tons U, 1,918 tons graphite, fuel elements each 36 in. long, 1·155 in. diameter, 8 per channel. Cooled by compressed CO_2. Core is 40 ft. diameter, 25 ft. 8 in. high, 8 in. lattice pitch.
Berkeley (Gloucestershire)	560	213 tons U, fuel elements of U metal each 19 in. long, 1.1 in. diameter. Core is 48 ft. diameter, 30 ft. high. Cooled by compressed CO_2.

* Data from: K. Jay, *Nuclear Power*, London, Methuen, 1961.

catch fire (this actually happened to a very limited degree in what is now an obsolete type of reactor at Windscale, Cumberland in 1957). Air, water and compressed carbon dioxide have each been used as a coolant. The heat removed can be used to raise steam in a boiler outside the reactor, which can then be used to produce electricity in a conventional turbine.

(3) The relatively high temperatures and high neutron flux, associated with the high-power levels of modern reactors, place a severe strain upon the mechanical and chemical properties of constructional materials inside the reactor. Examples of new technological 'headaches' which arise when one attempts to extract the last ounce of performance out of a powerful reactor are:

(*a*) Metallic uranium fuel expands under prolonged neutron bombardment and may rupture the can of magnesium alloy in which it is contained. Fission product gases will then be released from the exposed uranium into the coolant circuit.

122

(b) Air cannot be used as a coolant with graphite moderator much above 200° C due to chemical oxidation reactions. Even carbon dioxide coolant at 300–400° C reacts to a small but appreciable degree with the graphite moderator under the influence of radiation.

(c) The uranium-235 content of the nuclear 'fuel' becomes 'burnt-up' at an appreciable rate, and at the same time the fission products build up within the fuel. These include several isotopes with high capture cross-sections for thermal neutrons (the so-called

Figure 9.6. Berkeley nuclear power station
(By courtesy of the United Kingdom Atomic Energy Authority)

'neutron poisons'), e.g. the following stable isotopes are formed: ^{83}Kr, fission yield 0·6 per cent, $\sigma = 205$ barns; ^{149}Sm, fission yield 1·3 per cent, $\sigma = 6·6 \times 10^4$ barns; ^{103}Rh, fission yield 2·9 per cent, $\sigma = 150$ barns.

The net result of these processes is a fall in the 'reactivity' of the fuel and in the average value of the multiplication constant, k, for the reactor. If the 'burn-up' of uranium-235 were allowed to proceed, the reactor would eventually cease to maintain a chain reaction, that is k would fall below unity even with all the control rods withdrawn. To maintain a steady operation of the reactor, the fuel has to be changed at intervals of a year or more. The degree of 'burn-up' varies from one fuel element to another throughout the reactor (e.g. it will be lower at the outer surface), and it is desirable to be able to discharge individual fuel elements from the reactor according to a planned schedule, whilst the reactor is at full power. This requirement involves complicated engineering equipment.

To a certain extent, the 'burn-up' of uranium-235 in a thermal reactor fuelled with natural uranium is offset by the growth of plutonium-239 from the uranium-239 which is produced by neutron capture in uranium-238. The amount of plutonium produced is less than that of the uranium-235 consumed, but it is nevertheless very important (a) for military purposes, as it may be cheaper to separate pure plutonium by chemical processes from spent uranium fuel than to separate the pure isotope 235 from natural uranium, (b) it represents a means of converting the relatively useless isotope 238 into a valuable fissionable material. To a certain extent, any thermal reactor fuelled with natural uranium is acting as a 'converter reactor' for the purpose of changing uranium-238 into plutonium. As an extension of this idea, it has been suggested that reactors could be designed to convert the natural isotope of thorium (232) into the more valuable material uranium-233. Thorium-232 is fissionable only by fast neutrons ($\sigma = 0.11$ at 2 MeV). It has several resonance peaks for the capture of epithermal neutrons at 20–80 eV, to produce thorium-233 which leads by two beta decays to uranium-233. This isotope may be separated from the thorium by chemical processing. It is of course necessary to maintain the thorium separate from any natural uranium or uranium-235 which is used as a nuclear fuel in the reactor.

$$^{232}_{90}\text{Th} + ^{1}_{0}\text{n} \rightarrow ^{233}_{90}\text{Th} \xrightarrow[t_{\frac{1}{2}}=22\,\text{min}]{\beta\ \text{decay}} ^{233}_{91}\text{Pa} \xrightarrow[t_{\frac{1}{2}}=27\cdot4\text{d}]{\beta\ \text{decay}} ^{233}_{92}\text{U}$$

ENRICHED URANIUM REACTORS

One reason for the large size of natural uranium graphite (or heavy water) moderated reactors is the necessity of efficient slowing down of fission neutrons below the resonance energies to avoid the 'resonance trap' before they encounter another fuel element, necessitating rather large spacing between fuel elements. The size of the reactor can be reduced by using ordinary water as the moderating material, since it is more efficient at slowing down neutrons (see Table 9.2). However, the relatively high thermal neutron capture in $'$H ($\sigma = 0.33$ barns) makes k_∞ for such a natural uranium fuelled system less than unity. This can be overcome if the uranium-238 content of the fuel is decreased by the addition of some of the pure isotope ^{235}U, which can be separated from ^{238}U by elaborate physical techniques such as the gaseous diffusion of the volatile compound uranium hexafluoride. 'Enriched uranium' reactors using water as a moderator and coolant can be small enough for specialized forms of marine propulsion, as in the United States submarine *Nautilus* and the U.S.S.R. icebreaker *Lenin*. The use of enriched uranium fuel makes other design improvements possible at the expense of increasing the cost of the fuel.

The high capital cost of the equipment at the moment does not make it attractive for normal commercial shipping, but this consideration is overruled in the case of a submarine by the capacity to operate under water for prolonged periods. The *Nautilus* put to sea in 1955 and is now one of a large fleet of nuclear submarines. Both *Nautilus* and *Lenin* (the latter made its maiden voyage in 1959) use enriched uranium oxide or uranium–zirconium alloy as fuel, clad in a specially corrosion-resistant zirconium alloy. The fuel elements are immersed in normal (not 'heavy') water under pressure. The water functions as a moderator *and* as a coolant, and the steam which is raised is used to drive turbines and so, indirectly, to propel the vessel. Similar reactors of larger size are also being built for land-based nuclear power stations in the U.S.A.

FAST FISSION REACTORS

If the degree of enrichment is sufficiently high, a chain reaction can be sustained with fast neutrons, for there is little chance of the loss of neutron energy by inelastic scattering in uranium-238, and the moderator is, of course, no longer required. Most of the neutrons have energies at or above 1 MeV, where the losses due to capture in uranium-235, plutonium-239, in fission products, in the coolant, or in structural materials such as steel are very small compared with fission in uranium-235 and plutonium-239.

If the core of the reactor is surrounded with a 'blanket' of natural uranium or of thorium, the fast neutrons which escape from the core may be slowed down and captured to produce plutonium-239 and uranium-233 respectively. Under the best conditions, it is likely that a composite reactor of this type can produce more thermally fissionable material in the 'blanket' than it consumes in the core. This possibility arises because of the favourable values of η, already quoted in Table 9.6, for the fast neutron systems, especially for plutonium-239 ($\eta = 2 \cdot 6$). The possible use of a fast reactor as a 'breeder' of fissionable material would not imply that one was getting 'something for nothing' but that one form of nuclear fuel (uranium-238) was being converted to a form which is more readily usable (plutonium-239). A thermal reactor cannot 'burn' more than about 1 per cent of the total uranium atoms, even allowing for the conversion of some uranium-238 to plutonium (of the order of 80 per cent of the uranium-235 that is consumed). A fast breeder reactor might 'burn' up to 50 per cent of the total uranium. A large experimental reactor of this type has been operating at low power at Dounreay in Scotland and reached a heat rating of 30 MW during the August of 1962. It is designed to operate eventually at a heat rating of 60 MW. Similar experiments are in progress in the United States and in Russia. At such relatively high power levels a major problem is that of removal of heat from the small core, and it is necessary to use liquid metals such as sodium in order to secure sufficient heat transfer. The control of the power level of a fast reactor cannot easily be effected with the usual absorbers like cadmium and boron which are used for thermal reactors, because of their inefficiency at higher energies (although at considerable expense it is in fact now possible to make control rods of the separated isotope, boron-10, with several times the cross-section of natural boron). Control is normally exercised either by withdrawing some fuel elements from the core or by withdrawing part of the reflector, to increase the escape of neutrons.

ATOMIC BOMBS

If the fuel elements in the core of a fast reactor were to melt and collect together in one liquid pool or solid lump (an exigency which is prevented by elaborate safety precautions) an uncontrolled fast neutron chain reaction would ensue. Because the multiplication constant would be considerably higher than unity, the effects of the 'delayed neutrons' would not be significant and the 'doubling time' would be very small—perhaps of the order of a microsecond. The rapid increase in power output would lead to a small explosion equivalent perhaps to a few hundred pounds of TNT, which would stop the nuclear reaction by increasing the average distance between uranium atoms.

An atomic bomb may be regarded as a fast reactor which is normally stored with the fuel elements sufficiently far apart to prevent *any* significant chain reaction but which can be detonated by the very sudden implosion of the separated components, possibly by means of a small charge of a chemical explosive and which can be held together as a critical mass sufficiently long for a considerable fraction of the uranium or plutonium nuclei to release energy in fission. Not only are large amounts of energy explosively released in this way, comparable with many thousands of tons of the chemical explosive TNT, but also the high temperatures (about $10^{7\circ}$ C) which are reached within the exploding bomb can be used as a 'trigger' for an even more powerful 'thermonuclear explosion' due to reactions of the type:

$$_1^3\text{H} + _1^1\text{H} \rightarrow _2^4\text{He} + 20 \text{ MeV}$$

$$_3^6\text{Li (possibly as lithium deuteride)} + _0^1\text{n} \rightarrow _1^3\text{H} + _2^4\text{He}$$

$$_1^3\text{H} + _1^2\text{H} \rightarrow _2^4\text{He} + _0^1\text{n} + 17 \text{ MeV}$$

Thermonuclear reactions are not necessarily chain reactions like those in a nuclear reactor or atomic bomb. The energy increment required to surmount the potential energy barrier between the hydrogen nuclei is supplied by the kinetic energy of these materials at temperatures of ten million degrees centigrade or more. Each fusion reaction releases energy greater than that required for initiation, and so helps to maintain the high temperatures necessary for the 'burning' of the light isotopes. The total energy release from a hydrogen bomb has been reported to be as high as that equivalent to 100 megatons of TNT. Although the thermonuclear reaction is not a neutron chain process, fast neutrons are released in some forms of the reaction, such as

$$_1^2\text{H} + _1^3\text{H} \rightarrow _2^4\text{He} + _0^1\text{n} + 17 \text{ MeV}$$

These fast neutrons can set off further fission chains in uranium-238, if this is present as a 'blanket' around the bomb. The so-called 'dirty' thermonuclear weapons probably are such that the extra explosive power, over and above that of a simple atomic weapon, comes from a fast fission process. This leads to a proportional increase in the production of fission products—some of which will ultimately appear as 'fall out' over most of the surface of the earth. Relatively 'clean' thermonuclear weapons may be those which achieve a high ratio of fusion to fission. Even so, the release of neutrons may produce some radioactive products by 'neutron activation' of hydrogen, carbon, sodium, etc.

THERMONUCLEAR POWER

Attempts are now in progress in all the larger industrial nations to 'harness' thermonuclear power, for example by inducing a sustained thermonuclear reaction of the type

$$_1^2\text{H} + _1^2\text{H} \rightarrow _1^3\text{H} + _1^1\text{H} + 4 \text{ MeV}$$

by passing powerful electric discharges through deuterium gas at low pressure. The ionized gas, at a low pressure and a high temperature, is called a 'plasma'. There are great practical difficulties to be overcome in raising the plasma to a sufficiently high temperature (of the order of $10^{8\circ}$ C) and in maintaining it at this temperature without loss of energy to the walls of the containing vessels. It is hoped to confine the plasma, by magnetic field for example, so that it does not touch the walls, and many difficult designs of equipment are under test, at the Culham Laboratory of the U.K.A.E.A. and in several American, Russian, French and German laboratories. If a sustained thermonuclear reaction is ever achieved in experimental equipment, it will then be desirable to find means of extracting the power which is liberated, for example, by withdrawing electric current which is induced in a secondary circuit, using the plasma as the primary of a transformer.

Thermonuclear reactions appear to be the means by which the sun and stars generate energy. This was first suggested by R. d'E. Atkinson and F. G. Houtermans in 1929, and in 1938 H. A. Bethe in the U.S.A. developed the details of this theory. Hydrogen nuclei are transformed to helium, with the evolution of 26·7 MeV per helium atom. The process does not occur directly, but takes two possible paths, one of which involves a carbon nucleus as an intermediary. It has been calculated that, in the sun, four million tons of matter are transformed into energy every second.

10

THE CHEMISTRY OF THE FISSION PRODUCTS AND OF THE TRANSURANIUM ELEMENTS

We have seen in the previous chapter that Fermi's experiments in 1934 on the irradiation of uranium with neutrons gave rise to a strong beta activity which was interpreted as due to one or more transuranium elements, of atomic numbers 93 and 94:

$$^{238}_{92}U + ^{1}_{0}n \rightarrow ^{239}_{92}U \rightarrow ^{239}_{93}(?) + \beta$$
$$\downarrow$$
$$^{239}_{94}(?) + \beta$$

The subsequent radiochemical study of the supposed transuranium elements was complicated by the presence of fission products and it was not until 1939–40 that it became possible to disentangle the two distinct sets of elements and their chemistry. Our present knowledge of the main nuclear reactions resulting from the neutron irradiation of natural uranium may be summarized:

$$^{235}_{92}U + ^{1}_{0}n \xrightarrow{\text{neutron capture}} ^{236}_{92}U$$

$$\text{As above} \xrightarrow{\text{fission}} \text{Fission products (Table 10.1)}$$

$$^{238}_{92}U + ^{1}_{0}n \xrightarrow{\text{neutron capture}} ^{239}_{92}U$$

$$^{239}_{92}U \xrightarrow{t_{\frac{1}{2}}=23 \text{ min}} ^{239}_{93}Np + \beta$$

$$^{239}_{93}Np \xrightarrow{t_{\frac{1}{2}}=2\cdot3 \text{ days}} ^{239}_{94}Pu + \beta$$

$$^{239}_{94}Pu \xrightarrow{t_{\frac{1}{2}}=24,300 \text{ years}} ^{235}_{92}U + ^{4}_{2}He$$

The products include (a) inactive isotopes or isotopes of very low specific activity, such as ^{236}U and several of the fission products, such as the molybdenum isotopes $^{95-98}Mo$; (b) beta and gamma active uranium isotopes and transuranium elements (^{239}U, $^{239}_{93}Np$) and fission products ($^{89-90}_{38}Sr$, $^{141}_{58}Ce$ and $^{144}_{58}Ce$); alpha active transuranium elements, e.g. $^{239}_{94}Pu$. Other isotopes in this category arise by secondary nuclear reactions and include $^{237}_{93}Np$ ($t_{\frac{1}{2}} = 2\cdot2 \times 10^6$ y), $^{240}_{94}Pu$ ($t_{\frac{1}{2}} = 6,600$ y) and $^{241}_{95}Am$ ($t_{\frac{1}{2}} = 470$ y).

Table 10.1. Main Isotopes Produced by the Fission of Uranium

Classification in Periodic Table	Element	Isotopes	Radiation	Half-life	Notes on any daughter products which soon grow (see pp. 55–6)
Group 0	Krypton	82 83 84 85 86	β, γ	10·4 y	
	Xenon	129 131 132 133 134 136	β, γ	5·3 d	
Group 1A	Caesium	133			Secondary product by capture in 133 is 134; β, γ, 2·3 y
		135 136 137	β β, γ β, γ	2×10^6 y 13 d 30 y	Ba*–137; IT, 2·6 min
Group 2A	Strontium	86 87 88 89 90	β, γ β	54 d 28 y	Y-90; β, 64 h
	Barium	135 136 137 138 140	β, γ	12·8 d	La-140; β, γ 40·2 h
Group 3A	Yttrium	89 90 91	β β, γ	64 h 58 d	
	Lanthanum	139 140	β, γ	40·2 h	
	Cerium	140 141 142 143 144	β, γ β, γ β, γ	32 d 33 h 285 d	Pr-144; β, γ, 17 min
	Praseodymium	141 143	β	13·8 d	
	Neodymium	143 144 145 146 147 148 150	α β, γ	2×10^{10} y 11·6 d	

Table 10.1—(*Contd.*)

Classification in Periodic Table	Element	Isotopes	Radiation	Half-life	Notes on any daughter products which soon grow (*see pp. 55–6*)
Group 3A (*Contd.*)	Promethium	147	β	2·6 y	
		149	β, γ	50 h	
		151	β, γ	27 h	
	Samarium	147	α	$1·3 \times 10^{11}$ y	
		149			
		151	β, γ	80 y	
		152			
		153	β, γ	47 h	
		154			
	Europium	151			
		153			
		155	β, γ	1·7 y	
		156	β, γ	15 d	
Group 4A	Zirconium	90			
		91			
		92			
		93	β, γ	9×10^5 y	
		94			
		95	β, γ	65 d	Nb-95; β, γ, 35 d
		96			
Group 5A	Niobium	93			
		95	β, γ	35 d	
Group 6A	Molybdenum	95			
		96			
		97			
		98			
		99	β, γ	67 h	
Group 6B	Tellurium	125			
		126			
		127*	IT	110 d	Te-127; β, 9·3 h
		128			
		129*	IT	33 d	Te-129; β, γ, 72 min
		130			
		131	β, γ	30 h	
		132	β, γ	77 h	I-132; β, γ, 2·3 h
Group 7A	Technetium	99	β	$2·1 \times 10^5$ y	
Group 7B	Iodine	127			
		129	β, γ	$1·7 \times 10^7$ y	
		131	β, γ	8·05 d	
Group 8	Ruthenium	99			
		101			
		102			
		103	β, γ	40 d	
		106	β	1·0 y	Rh-106; β, γ, 30 sec
	Rhodium	103			
		105	β, γ	36 h	

Notes: 1. Fission product isotopes with a chain fission yield of less than 0·1 per cent or of half-life less than 1 day have not been included.

2. Values for the fission yields of the individual isotopes have not been included, because the apparent yield will depend on the length of the decay period following the fission. Approximate values for the *maximum* yield of any given mass number may be taken from *Figure 9.4.*

FISSION] PRODUCTS

The fission products (Table 10.1) cover a wide range of elements, spread over the middle of the Periodic Table. One of the elements, promethium, was previously unknown—that is, the study of fission filled in a gap in the Periodic Table. Another element, technetium, was made available in milligram amounts for the first time. In the other cases the fission products are isotopes of known elements whose chemistry had been studied, but their investigation nevertheless has important consequences for inorganic chemistry and for other branches of science, for the following reasons:

(1) That form of the element which is isolated from the fission of uranium has a different composition from that of the naturally occurring element, e.g. natural caesium occurs only as the stable isotope, 133, whereas the fission product caesium is a mixture of 133, 134, 135, 136 and 137.

(2) The radioactive properties of many of the fission product isotopes have led to important applications which would not have been possible with the natural element; for example, the use of ^{90}Sr, ^{131}I and ^{137}Cs in hospitals for treatment or diagnosis and the use of ^{85}Kr in low intensity light sources (Chapter 11).

(3) The technical importance of some of the fission product elements, for example during the industrial processes of chemical separation of uranium and plutonium from irradiated uranium, has led to intensive studies of their inorganic chemistry which have resulted in advances in basic knowledge, notably in the chemistry of ruthenium and the rare earths.

SEPARATION OF URANIUM, FISSION PRODUCTS AND TRANSURANIUM ELEMENTS

The separation of plutonium from natural uranium which had received a prolonged bombardment with neutrons was first undertaken as part of the military exploitation of atomic energy in the United States. Plutonium continues to be separated for use in weapons, also as a possible fuel for fast 'breeder' reactors (p. 125) and as a source of the higher transuranium elements (p. 145). The uranium, which has become depleted in the 235 isotope, is usually recovered and is used again after removing some of the excess uranium-238 by gaseous diffusion of the hexafluoride. Certain transuranium elements such as neptunium-237 and americium-241 are extracted as by-products from the fission-product wastes.

All large-scale processes for the chemical processing of irradiated uranium begin by dissolving the metal in nitric acid in the presence of oxygen (so-called fumeless dissolving):

$$2U + 3O_2 + 4HNO_3 = 2H_2O + 2UO_2(NO_3)_2$$

The separation process subsequently depends upon the different extent to which uranium, plutonium and the fission products are extracted from solution in dilute nitric acid by solvents such as

Table 10.2. Distribution Coefficients between 20 per cent T.B.P. in a Hydrocarbon Diluent and 1 M and 6 M Nitric Acid at 20–25°C

	1M HNO$_3$	6M HNO$_3$
UO$_2^{2+}$	5	30
PuO$_2^{2+}$	0·7	3
Pu^{4+}	1·3	20
Pu^{3+}	0·015	0·01
Zr^{4+}	0·01	1
Ce^{4+}	0·01	0·2
RuNO (NO$_3$)$_x$	10	0·01
Y^{3+}	0·01	0·02

Data from: J. M. Fletcher, Volume 9, *Proceedings of the First United Nations International Conference on the Peaceful Uses of Atomic Energy, United Nations*, 1955, 459.

tributyl phosphate (TBP) (Table 10.2). An additional variable is provided by the adjustment of the valency state of the dissolved plutonium to III (reduction with ferrous or uranous salts or with hydrazine nitrate) or a mixture of higher valencies (IV and VI) by oxidation with dichromate, or to IV by oxidation with hydrogen peroxide or with nitrous acid.

It is possible to extract uranium as nitrate complexes of UO_2^{2+} and plutonium (as nitrate complexes of Pu^{4+}) from 3M HNO_3, free from most of the fission products. The plutonium may then be removed from the organic phase, without uranium, by shaking it with 3M nitric acid and a ferrous salt, when trivalent plutonium nitrate passes into the aqueous phase. The uranium nitrate may finally be removed from the organic solvent by shaking with water.

The account given above of the separation process is greatly simplified. A single partition between dilute nitric acid and the solvent does not give a high enough degree of purification, and banks of countercurrent mixer–settler units or packed columns are used to give a complete fractionation. The separated uranium and plutonium require one or more cycles of further purification by solvent extraction or ion exchange to remove every trace of the fission products.

Neptunium-237 (which is formed by the action of fast neutrons on uranium-238 to the extent of less than 1 per cent of the plutonium) has been isolated on a gramme scale as a by-product. It mainly accompanies uranium and plutonium into the solvent, as Np^{4+}, which is not reduced by ferrous salts in acid solution and remains with the uranium in the solvent and follows it into the water wash, where, at low acidity, it is oxidized to NpO_2^+. This valency state does *not* follow uranium on subsequent solvent extraction (uranium purification) and may be recovered by absorption on an anion exchange resin, as nitrate complexes of NpO_2^+ and of Np^{4+} at nitrate ion concentration of 7M, followed by elution with a small volume of 0·1M HNO_3.

Examples of the new chemical knowledge arising from the study of the fission products will be taken from the chemistry of the rare earths and technetium.

THE RARE EARTHS

Seven rare earth elements (lanthanum, cerium, praseodymium, neodymium, promethium, samarium, and europium) are amongst the main products of fission, together with another Group 3 element, yttrium, which closely resembles the rare earths in its chemical properties. As a rare earth group, these 8 elements are easily isolated from the other fission products and from uranium and other heavy elements, by repeated precipitations of their insoluble trivalent hydroxides, fluorides and oxalates. It may be necessary to add small amounts of, say, lanthanum as a 'carrier'. Cerium may be separated from the other members of the group as it is readily oxidized, for example by boiling with potassium bromate in acid solution, to a quadrivalent state, which forms an iodate, $Ce(IO_3)_4$, insoluble in dilute nitric acid, in which medium the trivalent rare earth iodates remain in solution. The separation of the remaining 7 elements had, before 1942, only been accomplished using relatively large quantities, by means of the fractional crystallization of such double salts as ammonium or sodium lanthanum nitrate or sulphate, e.g. $NaLa(SO_4)_2$. The lighter rare earths, such as cerium, tend to collect in the insoluble fraction: the salts of the heavier rare earths (and also the related element, yttrium) are rather more soluble. The fractions which are isolated in this way have to be boiled with alkali to precipitate the rare earth hydroxides, which are then redissolved in hydrochloric acid and subjected to a further fractionation as the sodium rare earth sulphate. This process is very laborious and it is difficult to obtain a complete separation between adjacent members of the series.

G. E. Boyd, W. E. Cohn and other chemists in the United States in 1942, applied the method of ion exchange to separate the fission product rare earths, and refinements of their method have since been used for the separation of the complete list of 14 rare earths, not only on a small scale but even for the production of kilogram samples of pure rare earths (by F. H. Spedding at Iowa State College).

An ion exchange material is normally an insoluble synthetic resin which (for cation exchange) contains free acidic groups such as —OH (phenolic), —CO_2H (carboxylic) and —SO_3H (sulphonic acid). If a solution of lanthanum chloride is poured on to a column of cation exchange resin, lanthanum ions replace hydrogen ions and become firmly held on the resin. If the resin is then washed with, say, 3M hydrochloric acid, then a very small fraction of the lanthanum is released, according to the Law of Mass Action:

$$La\text{–}resin + 3HCl = H_3\text{–}resin + LaCl_3$$

$$[La\text{–}resin][HCl]^3/[H_3\text{–}resin][LaCl_3] = K$$

If the quantities of lanthanum are very small compared with the available sites for cation exchange on the resin, then [H_3–resin] is constant and the important practical factor is the ratio [La–resin]/[$LaCl_3$] which is usually expressed as a distribution coefficient, K_d, = amount of solute absorbed per g of resin/amount of solute remaining per ml of solution. The higher the value of K_d the harder it is to remove lanthanum from the resin. If one applied a mixture of the rare earth elements to the resin, followed by prolonged washing with 3M hydrochloric acid, then some separation of the rare earths would be achieved and they would tend to group themselves in bands down the column. It is found that the value of K_d decreases with atomic weight from lanthanum ($Z = 57$) to lutetium, ($Z = 71$) but the differences tend to be masked by the high numerical values of K_d, which in the case of La are 97 and 2,200 for 3M and 1M HCl respectively. All the rare earths are so strongly held on the resin that it is difficult to achieve any significant degree of separation between them. The new technique introduced by the United States chemists in 1942 was the use of complexing agents rather than hydrochloric acid as the elutriant for displacing the rare earths from their initial site of absorption at the top of the column. A typical reagent is 5 per cent citric acid–ammonium citrate buffer, pH 3·65. Two factors are involved here. First, the equilibrium for the reactions shown below is governed by the concentration of hydrogen ions—by the pH of the buffer:

$$LaR_3 + NH_4^+ + 2H^+ = La^{3+} + NH_4R + 2HR \qquad (10.1)$$

$$La^{3+} + H_2Cit^- = [LaCit.] + 2H^+ \qquad (10.2)$$

Overall:

$$LaR_3 + (NH_4)H_2Cit. = [LaCit.] + NH_4R + 2HR \qquad (10.3)$$

where R represents one equivalent of the acidic groups which form part of the resin; Cit. represents the citrate anion, derived from tribasic citric acid, $CH_2CO_2H \cdot C(OH)CO_2H \cdot CH_2CO_2H$.

The ratio of $[LaR_3]/[LaCit.]$, i.e. the value of K_d, can be adjusted by the control of the pH of the buffer, so that K_d is moderately low (typical values: 1·43, 2·7, 4·3 for Pr, Ce and La respectively, in 5 per cent citrate at pH 3·65). That is, the rare earths are not *too* firmly held on the resin. If the citrate solution is allowed to flow continuously down the column, the lanthanum ions (initially absorbed at the top) are taken into solution as the soluble lanthanum citrate and are then re-absorbed on fresh sites lower down the column. The process is analogous to the successive evaporation and condensation of a volatile constituent of a mixture under distillation as it passes through a multi-stage fractionating column. At slow flow rates, the effective number of stages present in a column of resin can be very high—several thousand per foot.

The second factor is that the K values differ for the various rare earths. In effect K depends on (*a*) the affinity of the resin for, say, lanthanum, and (*b*) the strength of the lanthanum citrate complex. Fortunately these effects combine to magnify the differences in K between individual rare earths. The resin affinity *decreases* and the strength of the citrate (or other) complex *increases* along the series: La, Ce, Pr, Nd, Sm, Eu, etc.

Imagine a mixture of rare earths, initially absorbed in a narrow band at the top of a column of resin. Citrate buffer solution is allowed to pass slowly through the column. The 'band' of absorbed rare earths will be displaced and will slowly move down the column, as described above for the single element, lanthanum. Because of the differences in the values of K, and of the large number of 'theoretical stages' contained in the column, the individual rare earths will be fractionated and will move down the column as a set of overlapping bands. Europium will travel in the leading band, and lanthanum in the last band. Under the best conditions (of length of column, pH of buffer, temperature, etc.) a complete separation will be achieved by the time each band reaches the bottom of the column and is washed out by the continuing flow of buffer, into a separate container. The separation of radioactive rare earths is particularly easy to demonstrate, if the eluant from the column is continuously monitored with a Geiger counter (*Figure 10.1*), with a steady flow rate and persisting over several days. The results shown in *Figure 10.1* reveal a complete separation of La, Ce and Pr, the last named element being the first to leave the column.

The ion-exchange method of separation of individual cations

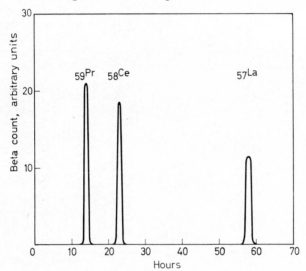

Figure 10.1. Separation of rare earth elements by ion exchange
(F. W. Cornish, by courtesy of *Canad. J. Chem.*)

which we have described is applicable to medium or to ultra-small quantities of rare earths (or indeed of other chemical elements). On the medium scale (hundreds of grammes) attention must be paid to the possible 'saturation' of all the available absorption sites on part of the resin: the remedy is to use wider columns, of up to 4 in. in diameter. On the small scale, the technique works with sub-microscopic amounts of metallic cations and is limited in practice only by the analytical techniques available to detect the material in various fractions. In dealing with fission products and with the transuranium elements, the technique is particularly valuable because it does not require a 'carrier' element. Refinements of the technique, using micro-columns, fractions collected as individual drops, and with improved complexing agents such as ammonium α-hydroxy-isobutyrate have made it possible for Seaborg and his team at the University of California (1954) to separate the higher transuranium elements and even to identify new members of the actinide series (*Figure 10.2*).

Returning to the subject of the rare earths, the missing element (atomic number 61) between neodymium and samarium was identified in fission products by J. A. Marinsky, L. E. Glendenin and C. D. Coryell in 1945, as a beta active fission product of half-life

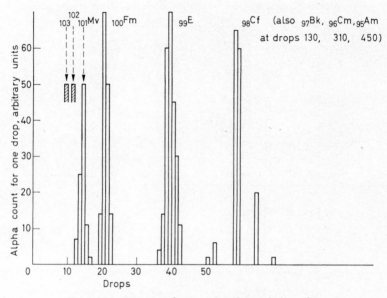

Figure 10.2. Separation of transuranium elements by ion exchange
(Data from Katz and Seaborg, 1957)

3·7 years. Milligramme quantities of this isotope of element 61 were eventually prepared in a pure state, and the mass number and atomic number were determined to be 147 and 61 respectively, by mass spectrometry and by the measurements of the wavelengths of the K-lines of the characteristic X-ray spectrum. The name Promethium was accepted by the International Union of Chemistry in 1949 (Prometheus: from Greek mythology, a god who brought fire from heaven to earth for the use of man).

TECHNETIUM

E. Segrè had worked with Fermi at Rome in 1934 when the use of neutrons to transmute one chemical element into another was demonstrated (Chapter 8). It was known that a related set of nuclear reactions could be produced by bombarding elements with deuterons from a cyclotron. In 1937, working at the Royal University, Palermo, where Segrè had moved in 1937, C. Perrier and E. Segrè investigated the chemical nature of the beta emitters which were present in a sample of molybdenum metal, which had been exposed to bombardment by deuterons and neutrons for several months in Prof. E. O. Laurence's cyclotron at the Radiation Laboratory of the University of California. The molybdenum was dissolved in aqua regia and the solution was subjected to a chemical fractionation, after the addition of inactive zirconium, niobium, manganese and rhenium as 'carriers'. The first three elements, together with the molybdenum, were recovered as inactive compounds. The rhenium carried a beta activity, of several months half-life, which like rhenium, was precipitated by H_2S from acid solution and could be redissolved in hydrogen peroxide. Like rhenium, the activity had a volatile oxide which could be absorbed in an alkaline solution. It was not, however, chemically identical with rhenium, for it did not distil as the chloride from 80 per cent H_2SO_4 in a stream of HCl at 200° C.

Perrier and Segrè ascribed the beta activity to one or more isotopes of the element of atomic number 43, which element had been tentatively recognized by I. and W. Noddack in 1925. A firm identification of a radioactive isotope of element 43 came in 1939, from G. T. Seaborg and E. Segrè (the latter now working at the Radiation Laboratory at California). Experiments on freshly irradiated molybdenum revealed a 67 h beta activity due to an isotope of molybdenum, leading to a 6·6 h activity which could be separated chemically from molybdenum on rhenium as a carrier. The 6·6 h activity was shown to be an isomeric transition from a metastable to a more stable state. In such a transition, a gamma photon is emitted (in this case of energy 0·136 MeV) which undergoes internal conversion by K capture to give mono-energetic electrons of energy 0·112 MeV and a characteristic X-radiation—which was shown to be that of an element of atomic number 43.

A longer-lived isotope of element 43 was later isolated (1947) from 4000 g of molybdenum which had been bombarded with neutrons in a nuclear reactor for 112 days. The yield of this element, technetium, was 10^{-4} g; the half-life is $2·1 \times 10^5$ years. This same isotope was isolated from fission products by D. C. Lincoln and W. H. Sullivan and independently by R. P. Schuman in laboratories associated with the United States Atomic Energy Commission in 1945. The mass number was determined by the mass spectrometer as 99, and the atomic number was verified as 43 by X-ray spectroscopy using a sample of about 1 mg. The sequence of nuclear reactions by which it is formed from molybdenum or from uranium is set out below:

$$^{235}_{92}U + ^{1}_{0}n \text{ (Fission yield = 6·1 per cent)} \rightarrow ^{99}_{42}Mo \xrightarrow{67\ h} ^{99}_{43}Tc + \beta$$

$$^{98}_{42}Mo + ^{1}_{0}n \rightarrow ^{99}_{42}Mo \xrightarrow{67\ h} (^{99}_{43}Tc) + \beta$$

$$(^{99}_{43}Tc) \xrightarrow[\text{Isomeric transition}]{6\ h} ^{99}_{43}Tc \xrightarrow{2\times10^5 y} ^{99}_{44}Ru \text{ (stable)} + \beta$$

The fission yield is high enough to mean that the waste fission products from nuclear reactors are now a major source of technetium (from the Greek 'teknetos'—artificial). Ruthenium and technetium are separated from the nitric acid solution of mixed fission products (after removing the uranium and the plutonium by solvent extraction) by the controlled precipitation of hydrated ferric oxide at pH2, leaving the alkaline earths and rare earths in solution. After redissolving the ferric oxide in acid, the technetium is selectively precipitated as tetraphenyl arsonium pertechnetate, $(C_6H_5)_4AsTcO_4$, and is finally recovered as ammonium pertechnetate, NH_4TcO_4. The element is now available from this source in gramme quantities.

The pure metal has been prepared by reducing ammonium pertechnetate with hydrogen, initially at a low temperature to avoid volatilization of the ammonium salt and finally at 500–600° C. The metal is a silver-grey spongy mass, tarnishing slowly in moist air. It may be converted to the volatile oxide, Tc_2O_7, in a stream of oxygen at 400–600° C. The oxide is soluble in water to give a pink acidic solution, which, on careful evaporation at room temperature, gives red-black crystals of $Tc_2O_7 \cdot H_2O$ (or $HTcO_4$). The solution of the heptoxide shows intense absorption peaks in the ultra-violet at 2470 Å and 2890 Å, which may be used for quantitative analysis. Gravimetric analysis can be made by using the stoichiometric compounds Tc_2S_7 (after extracting with carbon disulphide to remove free sulphur) or NH_4TcO_4 (which is stable in air at 100° C).

Generally, technetium resembles rhenium more than it does molybdenum or manganese. Unlike rhenium, however, the sulphide is soluble in 9M HCl, although precipitation is complete at a lower acidity, 2M. J. B. Gerlit of the U.S.S.R. has shown (1955) that the heptavalent technetium is reduced by HCl to the chloro complex of a tetravalent state, $TcCl_6^{2-}$. This reduction proceeds to some extent even in the cold, and is complete in half an hour at 75° C.

The valency states of aqueous solutions of technetium salts probably include 2, 4, 6 and 7.

There is some doubt as to whether or not the isotope $^{99}_{43}\text{Tc}$ occurs naturally in minerals. Herr has claimed to detect minute quantities in terrestrial rocks and also spectroscopically in the light from the sun and from certain stars. Vinogradov has postulated that the isotope is present in uranium ores, to the extent of 10^{-7} per cent of the uranium content, as a result of spontaneous fission of uranium-238.

TECHNOLOGICAL IMPORTANCE OF THE FISSION PRODUCTS

The fission products represent a limitation on the extended use of a given specimen of nuclear fuel in a reactor, because they absorb neutrons and expend their kinetic energy in processes which weaken the mechanical strength of the fuel and of the material in which it is canned.

The limited life of the fuel, due to fission product poisoning and mechanical damage, means that, for example, natural uranium fuel must be removed from the reactor while it still contains valuable uranium-235 and plutonium-239. It is desirable to recover uranium and plutonium by solvent extraction from acid solutions of the spent fuel. Certain of the longer-lived fission products, especially ruthenium-103 and -106, niobium-95 and zirconium-95, tend to follow uranium and plutonium to a small extent through the purification cycle. Considerable attention must be given to their chemical behaviour and sometimes auxiliary treatments are added to the main processes, for example, the use of hydrazine in hot dilute nitric acid to reduce extractable species of the type $\text{Ru(NO)(NO}_3)_3$ to inextractable complexes of Ru(IV), and the precipitation of manganese dioxide from dilute nitric acid to 'carry' traces of radiocolloidal niobium and zirconium.

The chemical separation gives rise to large quantities of fission product wastes as gases (krypton, xenon), as volatile materials (iodine), and as salts dissolved in solution.

The total quantity of radioactivity from non-volatile fission products, arising from the first eight generating stations of the British nuclear power programme to be completed by 1968, might well be as high as 10^9 curies per year (after 100 days cooling to allow short-lived isotopes to decay). This figure corresponds to the fission of about six tons of uranium per year to produce 5,000 MW of electrical power. The gaseous wastes, mainly the 10·4 y krypton-85, can be allowed to escape into the atmosphere or may be removed by scrubbing with carbon tetrachloride and storing by absorption on charcoal at low temperatures.

The non-volatile materials must be stored in a safe form for hundreds of years. The particularly objectionable isotopes are the long-lived strontium-90, caesium-137 and americium-241, all of which would be a hazard to public health if allowed to contaminate foodstuffs and water supplies. The present method of treatment is to evaporate the acid solutions as far as possible (a limit of about 150-fold evaporation is set by the sparing solubility of some of the constituents, e.g. ferric sulphate) and then to store the solutions in stainless steel tanks each holding 10^6 curies and each fitted with condensers, vapour filters and a ventilation stack. The tanks have to be fitted with cooling coils to remove the heat produced by the beta and gamma radiation, and they are contained in underground concrete caves.

In future it may be necessary to concentrate the material even further, and also to reduce the burden of watchful maintenance of these storage caves, which we are handing on to our descendants. Research into this problem has included the mixing of the solutions of the fission products with large quantities of natural clays, green-sands, chalks and other materials, followed by drying and finally sintering into a glassy material at $1,000°$ C. The fission products become incorporated in the glass in forms which resist any subsequent leaching by acids. This experimental process has not yet been tested on the required scale of millions of curies.

THE TRANSURANIC ELEMENTS

PREPARATION

Amongst the complicated radioactivities present in neutron irradiated uranium, and studied by E. Fermi and others from 1934, was a 23 min beta activity, which Hahn, Meitner and Strassmann in 1936 showed to be chemically inseparable from the parent uranium. It was natural to suppose that this activity was due to uranium-239, formed by a simple neutron capture from the most abundant isotope of natural uranium

$$^{238}_{92}U + ^{1}_{0}n \rightarrow {}^{239}_{92}U \ (\beta \text{ active, half-life 23 min})$$

The emission of a beta particle from an isotope of uranium must, by Soddy's Displacement Laws, lead to a hitherto unknown element of atomic number 93. No definite evidence for the presence of this new element was obtained until 1939, when E. M. McMillan at the University of California made a radiochemical study of a thin sample of neutron-irradiated uranium from which most of the fission products had escaped by 'recoil' (the fission fragments have enough kinetic energy to escape from the surface of irradiated uranium if the sample is sufficiently thin). Not only did he find the 23 min uranium activity, but also a 2·3 day low energy beta activity, which was chemically separable from uranium and which might have been a rare earth fission product—for example, it could be co-precipitated with lanthanum as the fluoride. Later (1940), McMillan and P. H. Abelson showed that the amount of 2·3 day activity did not decrease exponentially when the uranium was removed from the source of neutrons—it was not a direct fission product but a secondary product which was formed in increasing amounts as the uranium-239 decayed. Further chemical work showed differences between the 2·3 day isotope and the rare earths; for example, it could be oxidized with potassium bromate in dilute nitric acid to a different oxidation state, in which it did not co-precipitate with lanthanum fluoride but *did* co-precipitate with sodium uranyl acetate. This is therefore a new element, number 93, which in acid solution shows two different valency states, probably III and VI (the IV and V states are now also known). McMillan suggested the name 'Neptunium', symbol Np, after the planet Neptune which lies beyond Uranus in the solar system. Gramme quantities of a longer-lived neptunium isotope, $^{237}_{93}\mathrm{Np}$ (alpha emitter of half-life, $2·2 \times 10^6$ y), have since been isolated from waste fission products, arising from chemical processing plants. The neptunium-237 arises from the decay of a 6·8 day uranium-237, formed by fast neutron irradiation of uranium-238:

$$^{238}_{92}\mathrm{U} + ^1_0\mathrm{n} \rightarrow ^{237}_{92}\mathrm{U} + 2^1_0\mathrm{n}$$

$$^{237}_{92}\mathrm{U} \rightarrow ^{237}_{93}\mathrm{Np} + \beta$$

Reverting to the shorter-lived neptunium-239, it is obvious that just as the loss of a beta particle from a uranium isotope leads to element 93 (neptunium) so the loss of a beta particle from neptunium must lead to a hitherto unknown element of atomic number 94.

$$^{239}_{92}\mathrm{U} \xrightarrow{\beta} ^{239}_{93}\mathrm{Np} \xrightarrow{\beta} ^{239}_{94}\mathrm{Pu} \xrightarrow{\text{(alpha emitter)}}$$

Evidence for an isotope of atomic number 94 and mass number 239 was obtained by J. W. Kennedy, G. T. Seaborg, E. Segrè and A. C. Wahl at the University of California in 1941, and ton quantities have since been produced in nuclear reactors and are used in nuclear weapons.

Historically, the new element plutonium, named after the planet Pluto, was first prepared using the cyclotron in the winter of 1940–41 as the isotope of mass number 238, by the chain of reactions:

$$^{238}_{92}U + {}^{2}_{1}H \rightarrow {}^{238}_{93}Np + 2{}^{1}_{0}n$$

$$^{238}_{93}Np \xrightarrow[=2\cdot1d]{\text{half-life}} {}^{238}_{94}Pu + \beta$$

At this stage, the team of research workers included both E. M. McMillan and G. T. Seaborg: the former left to pursue radar research about the time that the United States entered the war, and consented to his pioneer work being followed up by G. T. Seaborg and others. It is interesting to note that although the early work on plutonium was pursued as a pure research problem with neither aid nor restriction by the government, the scientists themselves imposed a voluntary censorship, realizing the possible military uses of their discovery; for it had been already predicted that an isotope of mass 239 and atomic number 94 would be fissionable with thermal neutrons. Not only did they delay publication of their results by depositing secret communications dated 28 January and 7 March, 1941 with the editors of the *Physical Review* (published after the war, in 1946) but they even referred to plutonium in the laboratory under the code name of 'copper'.

The work on the preparation of new transuranium elements at the Radiation Laboratories of the University of California at Berkeley has continued since 1941 under Professor G. T. Seaborg, Professor E. Segrè (the original discoverer of technetium in 1937) and others, until element 103 was reached in 1961. Some contributions have also come from the National Laboratory of the University of Chicago, the Los Alamos Scientific Laboratory of the University of California, and a contribution from a joint team of Chicago, Harwell and Stockholm men working at the Nobel Institute, Stockholm. The isolation and investigation of these new elements has required large and expensive equipment (nuclear reactors, cyclotrons and other particle accelerators, remotely controlled and shielded laboratories and even thermo-nuclear explosions) and a co-ordinated team of specialist researchers, so that it is hardly possible to assign credit to isolated individuals (for example, the United States work on elements 99 and 100 involved 16 scientists and the Stockholm work on element 102 involved 8 scientists).

Some of the most important isotopes of the transuranium elements up to element 103 are included in Table 10.3, with some notes about the method of preparation. The following general points are worth noting.

The early work on neptunium and plutonium used neutrons or

Table 10.3. Preparation of the Transuranium Elements

Atomic number	Element	Symbol	Isotope	Half-life	Date	Preparation method
93	Neptunium	Np	239	2·35 d(β)	1939	$^{239}_{92}U \rightarrow {}^{239}_{93}Np + \beta$
			238	2·1 d (β)	1940	$^{238}_{92}U + {}^{2}_{1}H \rightarrow {}^{238}_{93}Np + 2{}^{1}_{0}n$
			237	2·2 × 10⁶ y	1942	$^{238}_{92}U + {}^{1}_{0}n \rightarrow {}^{237}_{92}U + 2{}^{1}_{0}n$
						$^{237}_{92}U \rightarrow {}^{237}_{93}Np + \beta$
94	Plutonium	Pu	239	2·4 × 10⁴ y	1941	$^{239}_{93}Np \rightarrow {}^{239}_{94}Pu + \beta$
95	Americium	Am	241	500 y	1944	$^{238}_{92}U + {}^{4}_{2}He \rightarrow {}^{241}_{94}Pu + {}^{1}_{0}n$
						$^{241}_{94}Pu \rightarrow {}^{241}_{95}Am + \beta$
96	Curium	Cm	242	162 d	1944	$^{239}_{94}Pu + {}^{4}_{2}He \rightarrow {}^{242}_{96}Cm + {}^{1}_{0}n$
97	Berkelium	Bk	243	4·6 h (K capture)	1949–50	$^{241}_{95}Am + {}^{4}_{2}He \rightarrow {}^{243}_{97}Bk + 2{}^{1}_{0}n$
98	Californium	Cf	245	44 min	1950	$^{242}_{96}Cm + {}^{4}_{2}He \rightarrow {}^{245}_{98}Cf + {}^{1}_{0}n$
99	Einsteinium	E	253	20 d	1952	$^{238}_{92}U + 15{}^{1}_{0}n \rightarrow {}^{253}_{92}U$
						$^{253}_{92}U \rightarrow {}^{253}_{99}E + 7\beta$
						(in a thermonuclear explosion)
100	Fermium	Fm	255	16 h	1953	$^{238}_{92}U + 17{}^{1}_{0}n \rightarrow {}^{255}_{92}U$
						$^{255}_{92}U \rightarrow {}^{255}_{100}Fm + 8\beta$
101	Mendelevium	Mv	256	1 h (K capture)	1955	$^{253}_{99}E + {}^{4}_{2}He \rightarrow {}^{256}_{101}Mv + {}^{1}_{0}n$
102	Nobelium	No	255	10 min	1957	$^{246}_{96}Cm + {}^{13}_{6}C \rightarrow {}^{255}_{102}No + 4{}^{1}_{0}n$
			254	3 sec	1958	$^{246}_{96}Cm + {}^{12}_{6}C \rightarrow {}^{254}_{102}No + 4{}^{1}_{0}n$
103	Lawrencium	Lw	257	8 sec	1961	$^{252}_{98}Cf + {}^{11}_{5}B \rightarrow {}^{257}_{103}Lw + 6{}^{1}_{0}n$

Based on data from Katz and Seaborg, 1957

The above elements were first prepared at the Berkeley laboratories of the University of California, with the exception of the following three elements:

Einsteinium, Fermium—isolated from the debris of a thermonuclear explosion by the Argonne National Laboratory, Chicago, the Los Alamos Scientific Laboratory, New Mexico and The Berkeley laboratories.

Nobelium (10 min isotope) isolated at Stockholm by a joint team from the Nobel Institute, Stockholm, the Argonne National Laboratory and the Atomic Energy Research Establishment, Harwell, England.

Their claim is still disputed.

deuterons to bombard uranium-238. This approach has been developed in three directions:

(a) Multiple neutron capture in uranium-238, by prolonged irradiations of plutonium-239 at the highest available neutron fluxes (10^{14} n cm^{-2} sec^{-1}) or by the examination of debris from the explosion of thermonuclear weapons which contained uranium-238. Isotopes such as $^{244}_{96}Cm$ and $^{253}_{98}Cf$ have been isolated from long irradiations of plutonium, and the elements einsteinium and fermium (atomic numbers 99 and 100 respectively) were first isolated in the radioactive debris from the United States thermonuclear test explosion 'Mike' in the Pacific Ocean in 1952. These two types of multi-neutron process may be set out diagrammatically as follows:

In a high flux reactor:

$$^{239}_{94}\text{Pu} + 4^1_0\text{n} \rightarrow {}^{243}_{94}\text{Pu} \xrightarrow[5\,\text{h}]{\beta} {}^{243}_{95}\text{Am (7950 y, }\alpha\text{)}$$

$$^{243}_{95}\text{Am} + {}^1_0\text{n} \rightarrow {}^{244}_{95}\text{Am} \xrightarrow[26\,\text{min}]{\beta} {}^{244}_{96}\text{Cm (19 y, }\alpha\text{)}$$

$$^{244}_{96}\text{Cm} + 5^1_0\text{n} \rightarrow {}^{249}_{96}\text{Cm} \xrightarrow[65\,\text{min}]{\beta} {}^{249}_{97}\text{Bk} \xrightarrow[290\text{d}]{\beta} {}^{249}_{98}\text{Cf (400 y, }\alpha\text{)}$$

$$^{249}_{98}\text{Cf} + 4^1_0\text{n} \rightarrow {}^{253}_{98}\text{Cf} \xrightarrow[19\,\text{d}]{\beta} {}^{253}_{99}\text{E (20 d, }\alpha\text{)}$$

$$^{253}_{99}\text{E} + {}^1_0\text{n} \rightarrow {}^{254}_{99}\text{E} \xrightarrow[36\,\text{h}]{\beta} {}^{254}_{100}\text{Fm (3·24 h, }\alpha\text{)}$$

In a thermonuclear explosion:

$$^{238}_{92}\text{U} + 15^1_0\text{n} \xrightarrow[\text{explosion}]{\substack{\text{Immediately}\\\text{following a}\\\text{thermonuclear}}} [^{253}_{92}\text{U}] \xrightarrow[\text{decays}]{\substack{\text{Successive}\\\beta}} {}^{253}_{99}\text{E (20 d, }\alpha\text{)} + 7\beta$$

$$^{238}_{92}\text{U} + 17^1_0\text{n} \xrightarrow[\text{explosion}]{\substack{\text{Immediately}\\\text{following a}\\\text{thermonuclear}}} [^{255}_{92}\text{U}] \xrightarrow[\text{decays}]{\substack{\text{Successive}\\\beta}} {}^{255}_{100}\text{Fm (22 h, }\alpha\text{)} + 8\beta$$

(*b*) The use of projectiles other than neutrons, for example alpha particles, deuterons, or the positive ions of rather heavier elements such as boron, carbon and oxygen. These positively charged projectiles require energies of the order of 30 MeV or more in order to overcome the electrostatic repulsion of the nucleus. Cyclotron-accelerated deuterons were used in the synthesis of transuranium elements in 1940 (neptunium, Table 10.3). Essentially the (d, n) or (d, 2n) reactions, like the (n, γ, followed by β) sequence, enable us to move forward by one atomic number. A larger step can be made by the use of high energy alpha particles,

$$^{239}_{94}\text{Pu} + {}^4_2\text{He} \rightarrow {}^{242}_{96}\text{Cm} + {}^1_0\text{n}$$

A logical extension of this approach is to fuse together a nucleus of uranium or of some available transuranium element with a nucleus of some element lower down the Periodic Table, such as carbon, which can be applied as a high energy beam of charged particles, by a cyclotron or other accelerating machine, e.g. the Heavy Ion Linear Accelerators, especially constructed for this purpose at the University of California and at Yale University.

$$^{246}_{96}\text{Cm} + {}^{13}_6\text{C (90 MeV)} \rightarrow {}^{255}_{102}\text{No (10 min, }\alpha\text{)} + 4^1_0\text{n}$$

This technique, which has also recently been applied to similar reactions of heavy elements in California and in Moscow, takes us several stages up the ladder in one operation.

(c) Examples which we have already quoted above make it clear that the starting material used for bombardment with charged ions has advanced with the years from uranium through plutonium to curium. The assault on elements of higher and higher atomic number has some resemblance to an assault by a team of climbers upon a high and difficult mountain. Starting from a base camp, loads are carried farther and farther up the mountain to establish successive camps until, from the final camp, the assault on the peak can be mounted. The size of the camps diminishes as they progress up the mountain. Similarly, the amounts of the transuranium elements which are at present available, range from perhaps tons of plutonium through gramme quantities of americium and curium, to micro or milligramme quantities of berkelium and californium. The higher elements have not yet been prepared in visible quantities, but have been recognized from the physical characteristics of their unstable atoms (e.g. alpha energies and spontaneous fission) and from the ion exchange behaviour of these atoms in the form of trivalent cations in aqueous solution (*Figure 10.2*). The experiments which led to the discovery of mendelevium were conducted with only 13 atoms of the product, and the controverted claim to the discovery of nobelium in 1957 detected only 20 atoms.

PROPERTIES

It was expected that the chemistry of the first four transuranium elements would resemble that of the elements rhenium, osmium iridium and platinum in Groups VII and VIII of the Periodic Table, just as actinium, thorium, protactinium and uranium resemble lanthanum, hafnium, tantalum and tungsten. In fact, the early work of E. M. McMillan and P. H. Abelson with neptunium showed that it was completely unlike rhenium. Generally, the transuranium elements which have been so far investigated form a unique series of elements, resembling uranium in some chemical properties and the rare earths in others. Like uranium, they show valency states, in aqueous solution, of III, IV, V and VI, and many of the solutions are intensely coloured (Table 10.4). The V and VI valency states are oxygenated, as in UO_2^+ and UO_2^{2+}.

The relative stability of each oxidation state which is indicated by printing the appropriate colour in italics in Table 10.4 varies from one member of the series to another, and may also be influenced by the addition of complexing agents, e.g. the sulphate ion, which tend to stabilize the IV state. Generally the higher valencies become progressively less important as one moves along the series.

Table 10.4. Colours of Aqueous Solutions of Uranium and Transuranium Elements

Element	Valency state			
	III	IV	V	VI
Uranium	Red	Green	—	*Yellow*
Neptunium	Blue to purple	Yellow-green	*Green*	Pink to red
Plutonium	Blue to violet	*Tan to orange-brown*	—	Yellow to pink-orange
Americium	*Pink*	—	Yellow	Rum-coloured
Curium	*Colourless*	—	—	—

Data from: Katz and Seaborg, 1957

Curium and californium are trivalent in acidic aqueous solution but the solids CmO_2 and CmF_4 and the water stable Bk(IV) show that a higher valency has not completely disappeared.

When in the same valency state, the transuranium elements

Table 10.5. Ionic Data for Uranium and the Transuranium Elements

Element	Oxidation potential (Volts)	Ionic radius (Å)	
	III/IV, 1M $HClO_4$	(III)	(IV)
Uranium	+0·631	1·03	0·93
Neptunium	−0·155	1·01	0·92
Plutonium	−0·982	1·00	0·90
Americium	−2·44	0·99	0·89

From: Katz and Seaborg, 1957

are difficult to separate chemically except by ion-exchange (*Figure 10.2*) but they show a gradual change in properties along the series as shown in Table 10.5.

The decrease in ionic radius with increasing atomic number, noted in Table 10.5, is also a characteristic of the rare earths. For reasons of this kind, the transuranium elements are often said to belong to a rare-earth or 'actinide' series, starting below uranium with actinium. As the series builds up from actinium to element-103, the two outermost shells of valency electrons remain incomplete, whilst an inner shell is built up with only minor effects on the chemical properties. In the case of the rare earths, the inner shell is a 4 shell which is built up from 18 to 32 electrons. In the case of the actinide elements the inner shell is

Table 10.6. Electronic Configurations of Actinides and Rare Earths

Element	Atomic number	Electron shells of gaseous atoms in ground states
Radon	86	2, 8, 18, 32, 18, 8
Francium	87	2, 8, 18, 32, 18, 8, 1
Radium	88	2, 8, 18, 32, 18, 8, 2
Actinium	89	2, 8, 18, 32, 18, 9, 2
Thorium	90	2, 8, 18, 32, 18, 10, 2
Protactinium	91	2, 8, 18, 32, 20, 9, 2
Uranium	92	2, 8, 18, 32, 21, 9, 2
Neptunium	93	2, 8, 18, 32, 22, 9, 2
Plutonium	94	2, 8, 18, 32, 24, 8, 2
Americium	95	2, 8, 18, 32, 25, 8, 2
Curium	96	2, 8, 18, 32, 25, 9, 2
Berkelium	97	2, 8, 18, 32, 26, 9, 2
Californium	98	2, 8, 18, 32, 28, 8, 2
Einsteinium	99	2, 8, 18, 32, 29, 8, 2
Fermium	100	2, 8, 18, 32, 30, 8, 2
Mendelevium	101	2, 8, 18, 32, 31, 8, 2
Nobelium	102	2, 8, 18, 32, 32, 8, 2
Lawrencium	103	2, 8, 18, 32, 32, 9, 2
Lanthanum	57	2, 8, 18, 18, 9, 2
Cerium	58	2, 8, 18, 20, 8, 2
Lutetium	71	2, 8, 18, 32, 9, 2

Based on data from Katz and Seaborg, 1957

a 5 shell which is built up from 18 to 32 electrons. In either case, the series would be occupied by 14 elements.

The contraction of ionic radius with increasing atomic number, is said to be due to the increasing positive charge of the nucleus which pulls the outer electrons closer. The simultaneous addition of more electrons to a 'buried' shell does not completely offset this effect of an increased nuclear charge.

The electronic configurations given in Table 10.6 have been deduced from spectroscopic and magnetic measurements and they refer to the ground state of the gaseous atom. In chemical combination or as ions in solution the configurations will deviate from these 'ideal' lists. Furthermore, valency electrons can be drawn from more than one shell, a process called 'orbital hybridization'. These factors prevent one from inferring the chemical valency of the element *simply* by looking at the number of electrons in the outermost shell.

Neither the rare earths nor the actinides are uniformly trivalent, because the energy levels of the electrons available for this purpose are not far removed from those of certain other electrons in the outer shells.

The rare earths do not, however, often deviate from valency III—the most notable exceptions are cerium (IV), samarium (II) and europium (II). The actinides show many more deviations, especially in the early members of the series. In particular, thorium, protactinium and uranium resemble their homologues in Groups IVA, VA and VIA of the Periodic Table (hafnium, tantalum and tungsten). The subsequent members, neptunium, plutonium and americium resemble uranium (all show valencies of III, IV, V and VI, with varying degrees of stability). It is only from curium onwards that the series resembles the rare earths at all closely. It seems that the chemistry of the actinide elements cannot be described simply by drawing an analogy with the rare earths, nor completely correlated with the filling up of a 'buried' 5 shell from 18 to 32. There is clearly a considerable overlap of the stabilities of some of the electron levels in shells 5, 6 and 7.

11

THE USES OF RADIOACTIVE ISOTOPES

The naturally occurring radioactive isotopes were applied in several branches of science before the discovery of nuclear fission. From 1913, G. von Hevesy and F. A. Paneth in Germany used isotopes of lead to determine the solubility of lead salts and to study the uptake of lead by plants. Radium was used in hospitals, as far as it was available, for the destruction of cancerous tumours. One fruit of the discovery of nuclear fission and the subsequent construction of nuclear reactors has been the availability of a wide range of radioactive isotopes of almost all the known elements. These artificial radioactive isotopes may, for example, be produced by the slow neutron irradiation of a sample of the inactive element, or of a convenient compound, in a nuclear reactor, for example:

$$^{59}_{27}\text{Co (stable)} + ^{1}_{0}\text{n} \rightarrow ^{60}_{27}\text{Co}$$

$$^{60}_{27}\text{Co } (t_{\frac{1}{2}} = 5\cdot2 \text{ y)} \rightarrow ^{60}_{28}\text{Ni (stable)} + \beta + \text{gamma rays}$$

The current catalogue of the Isotope Division of the U.K.A.E.A. offers for sale a range of over a hundred different radioactive isotopes. Some of these isotopes, such as cobalt-60, are available in very intense strengths, up to several thousand curies, at a cost of a few pounds per curie,* compared with a single curie of radium which might have represented the entire stock of a large hospital before the discovery of nuclear fission. (The visit of Mme. Curie in 1921 to receive the gift from the women of the United States of 1 curie of radium for her further research work, was a major public occasion: the gift cost $100,000 and represented one-fiftieth of the total amount of separated radium in the U.S.A.) Even larger sources of radioactivity (2 to 3 million curies) can be provided by the waste fission products from the uranium fuel in the nuclear reactors, as in the irradiation facility adjacent to the Dido reactor at Harwell.

The use of radioactive isotopes has become commonplace in research laboratories (chemistry, physics, biology), in industry (textiles, steel, manufactured goods), in civil engineering (pipelines, coastal erosion) and in medicine (diagnosis and radiotherapy).

* A curie is a unit of radioactivity—it is defined as the disintegration rate of 1 g of radium, i.e. $3\cdot7 \times 10^{10}$ disintegrations per sec.

Innumerable practical examples could be quoted from each of these different fields (see for example, *Isotopes*, by J. L. Putman, in Pelican Books, first published in 1960). These diverse uses will be better understood if we examine those special features of radioactive isotopes which make them so outstanding as scientific tools. If these basic principles are well grasped, the reader should have no difficulty in appreciating any particular application in practical use and he or she may even be able to devise new applications to particular scientific and technical problems. The main uses are:

(1) Energy sources.
(2) Penetration.
(3) Uniform decay rate.
(4) Atomic labels.

     (*a*) Non-isotopic.
     (*b*) Isotopic, with complete exchange.
     (*c*) Isotopic, without immediate exchange.

ENERGY SOURCES

Radioactive isotopes release energy in the form of kinetic energy of recoil atoms, of alpha and beta particles and neutrons, and of quantum energy of electromagnetic radiation. Most of this energy may be captured as thermal energy by the source and its shield. Compounds of radium, for example, remain a few degrees centigrade warmer than the laboratory temperature. Plutonium-239, with a disintegration energy of about 5·2 MeV and a specific activity of 0·067 curies/g, emits energy at the rate of 0·002 W/g of plutonium metal. This heat output is hardly likely to be a practical source of energy, but isotopes of shorter half-life may be useful in exceptional circumstances.

The isotope plutonium-238 with a half-life of 90 years could supply 0·54 W/g and was used in an 'atomic battery' in the American earth satellite Transit 4A, which was placed in orbit on 29 June 1961. The battery weighs 4·6 lb. and produces 2·7 W of electrical power. Allowing for a relatively low efficiency of conversion of heat energy to electricity it appears that the battery must contain at least 50 g of plutonium-238. It has been suggested that waste fission products might be used as heat sources, since millions of curies are available from the used uranium fuel which is discharged from nuclear reactors. (1 million curies at 1 MeV per disintegration is equivalent to 6 kW.) The cost of shielding and other protective measures would be far greater than the commercial value of such sources. Separated fission product strontium-90 is a pure beta emitter and requires no heavy shielding—although stringent precautions must be taken to avoid leakage. Atomic batteries using thousands of curies of strontium-90 as strontium titanate in close contact with a lead telluride thermocouple have been constructed to deliver up to 60 W of electrical power. The Martin Company of Baltimore, U.S.A., has made several batteries, each with 10^4–10^5 curies of strontium-90 as strontium titanate. These have been used at unmanned polar weather stations, in a satellite and in a lighthouse.

The isotopes krypton-85 ($t_{\frac{1}{2}} = 10 \cdot 4$ y) and hydrogen-3 (tritium $t_{\frac{1}{2}} = 12 \cdot 3$ y) are beta emitters, which can be applied to generate a weak source of light for marker beacons and signal lamps, by allowing the beta particles to bombard a layer of zinc sulphide or other phosphor. It is possible to produce beacons which are visible for half a mile, using krypton-85 confined in a shallow container which is lined with a phosphor. These beacons are independent of power supplies and should need no maintenance.

Strenuous attempts have been made to find some industrial use for large radiation sources, such as waste fission products and the cobalt-60 that can be produced in nuclear reactors. For example, the energy released in radioactive decay might be used to accelerate some valuable chemical reaction. The reaction of benzene with chlorine to form the insecticide, benzene hexachloride, and also the polymerization of ethylene to give the plastic material, polyethylene, are examples of chemical reactions which are accelerated by irradiation with gamma rays. Nevertheless, the use of large radiation sources appears at the present time to show insufficient commercial advantage over the use of ultra-violet light (for benzene hexachloride) or of chemical catalysts (for polyethylene).

The main use for the energy output of large radiation sources remains a purely destructive one—the sterilization or killing of insects, bacteria or cancer cells.

Weevils in stored grain can be killed (50 per cent mortality within 24 h) by exposure to a radiation dose of about 400,000 rads (this unit is defined on p. 172). Hospital blankets do not stand up well to steam sterilization, but can be sterilized sufficiently well to reduce cross-infection by viruses, by 100,000 to 200,000 rads. The multiplication of insect pests can sometimes be greatly reduced by releasing large numbers of male insects, specially bred for the purpose and sterilized by about 20,000 rads. For example, the screw-worm fly in the island of Curaçao was controlled in 1954 by the release of millions of sterilized male flies. The female screw-fly mates only once, and the choice of a sterile male stops the breeding cycle.

153

A major use of the destructive energy from large radiation sources is the controlled application of a narrow beam of gamma rays (*Figure 11.1*), usually from a heavily shielded source of several thousand curies of cobalt-60 or caesium-137, to destroy tumours or to prevent their further growth. This is an extension of the previous use of radium and of X-rays, which use dates back to the early years of this century. The radioisotope irradiation units possess

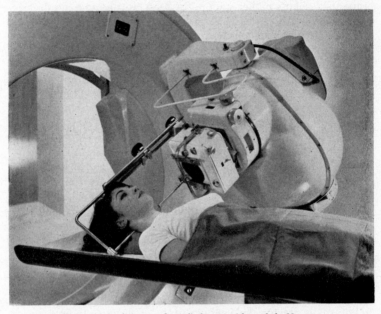

Figure 11.1. Apparatus for radiotherapy with a cobalt-60 source
(By courtesy of Associated Electrical Industries Ltd.)

the advantage over the conventional type of X-ray machine of emitting a more penetrating radiation (cobalt-60 gives 1·33 and 1·17 MeV, caesium-137 gives 0·66 MeV, a conventional X-ray therapy machine gives 0·25 MeV) which can be used to attack deep-seated tumours without causing excessive irradiation to the skin and surface tissues. Their advantage over radium (which has various gamma energies up to 1·8 MeV) is their relative cheapness— hospitals do not usually possess more than a few curies of radium, whereas 1,000 curie units of cobalt-60 have become fairly common, and 1,000 curie units of caesium-137 are also available.

PENETRATION

The last example has included some reference to the penetrating powers of gamma rays into body tissues. The fact that beta particles and gamma rays can penetrate materials to a greater or lesser degree has led to a variety of industrial applications.

Buried or otherwise inaccessible objects can be detected by receiving signals from a gamma emitter, which can penetrate through the thickness of a pipeline or through several feet of earth. For

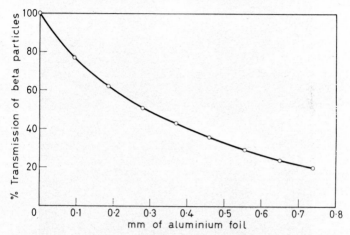

Figure 11.2. The absorption of beta particles by aluminium. Beta source: strontium-89 (maximum energy, 1·48 MeV)

example, buried pipelines which convey petroleum fuels from the refineries to storage depots are cleaned from dirt and rubble at intervals by the passage (under hydraulic pressure) of a 'go-devil' or 'pig', which has a series of scrapers. Occasionally a go-devil remains stuck in a pipe and the engineers need to locate the site of the blockage in order to dig up the pipe and free the obstruction. A source of 0·2 curies of cobalt-60 can be incorporated in a second 'go-devil' which is sent after the first, until it comes to rest at the obstruction. The radioactive source can be detected, even at a depth of 3 ft. using a portable Geiger counter at ground level.

In the last example, the gamma rays from cobalt-60 would of course be considerably attenuated by 3 ft. of earth, which is unimportant so long as a sufficient signal remains. Another important group of applications involves the measurement of the actual degree of attenuation of gamma rays or beta particles in their passage through an absorber (*Figure 11.2*). Such measurements

155

can be used to determine the thickness of paper, plastics and thin
metal sheets during production; for example, the thickness of thin
steel sheet emerging from a high-speed rolling mill can be monitored
continuously. Beta ray sources are used for paper and cardboard
and for $\frac{1}{16}$ in. steel sheet; the more penetrating gamma rays are
used for thicknesses up to 3 or 4 in. of steel.

Another important industrial use of the penetrating radiation

Figure 11.3. Radiograph of a watch taken with iridium-192
(By courtesy of United Kingdom Atomic Energy Authority)

from gamma emitters is to supplement the use of X-rays for obtain-
ing radiographs ('shadow photographs') of castings, weldings, etc.
(*Figure 11.3*). Radium has long been used for this purpose, but the
newer sources are far cheaper. The great advantage of gamma ray
sources over X-ray machines is their portability and small size—they
can, for example, be used inside pipelines to test the welds, wrapping

the photographic film around the outside of the pipe. This convenience of manoeuvrability is lost if the source strength is more than about a curie, because heavy shielding would be required. At the level of one curie, the total flux of gamma rays striking the object under test is about a factor of 100 lower than the flux from a conventional X-ray machine. That is, the radiographs are considerably slower with a gamma source. Often, however, the exposure may be allowed to proceed overnight, when the plant is not in use.

UNIFORM DECAY RATE

The equations given in Chapter 5:

$$N = N_0 \cdot e^{-\lambda t} \quad \text{and} \quad -dN/dt = \lambda N$$

where $\qquad\qquad\qquad \lambda = 0 \cdot 693/t_{\frac{1}{2}}$

assume that the decay constant, λ, remains a true constant over any interval of time. This has been tested experimentally in two ways. First, with isotopes of medium half-life, we may conveniently measure $-dN/dt$, the rate of radioactive decay, over a range of two powers of ten, which corresponds to between six and seven half-lives. Over this range the half-life is found to be constant. Second, with isotopes of very long half-life (e.g. uranium-238, $4 \cdot 51 \times 10^9$ years), we can verify that $-dN/dt$ changes by less than the experimental error of one part in a thousand over the duration of the experiments, and that it is unaffected by any physical or chemical changes which are brought about in the laboratory tests by the experimenter. It is then reasonable to assume that the law holds for isotopes such as uranium over those long periods of time which are inaccessible to the experimenter but which are comparable with the half-life, in this particular case 4,510,000,000 years. If this assumption holds good, we can use the extent of radioactive decay in a sample of uranium as a measure of lapsed time. If we could (hypothetically) compare the specific alpha activity of two purified samples of uranium, one prepared in 1962 and the other prepared thousands of millions of years ago, the results would enable us to calculate the exact lapse of time between the two preparations. Such an experiment is, of course, impossible in these actual terms. However, a similar result can be obtained today if we measure not only a purified sample of uranium, but also a sample of uranium mineral which contains all the daughter products of the radioactive decay. Particularly, we can measure the amount of lead-206, which is the stable end-product of the chain

157

of decay processes which start with uranium-238. We need not confuse these with traces of ordinary lead 204, 206, 207, 208 in the proportions $1 \cdot 3 : 26 : 21 : 52$ which may be present as an impurity, for mass spectrometric analysis will reveal the amount of *excess* lead-206, i.e. radiogenic lead. The atoms of lead-206 which we find must have started life as atoms of uranium-238. It is now possible to calculate what time has elapsed since the uranium-238 started to decay, assuming that no lead-206 was initially present.

$$N_{238} = (N_{238} + N_{206}) \cdot e^{-\lambda t}$$

or

$$1 = \left(1 + \frac{N_{206}}{N_{238}}\right) e^{-\lambda t}$$

A chemical or mass spectrometric measurement of the lead/uranium ratio may be used to calculate the ratio $K = N_{206}/N_{238}$ and the equation may be solved for t:

$$t = \frac{1}{\lambda} \log_e (1 + K)$$

The mass spectrometer may be used, not only to correct the lead analysis for the presence of traces of natural lead as impurity, but also to correct for the presence of other forms of radiogenic lead, i.e. lead-208, the end-product of the radioactive decay of thorium-232, and lead-207, the end product of the decay of uranium-235 and of protactinium-231. Values of t have been obtained by this method on samples of various minerals which contain uranium. Typical values range from 50 to 4,500 million years.

Geologists interpret this period of time as that which has elapsed since the solidification of the rocks from which the specimens were obtained, as from this time forward the decay products would be trapped in the solid rock. The highest value obtained on any mineral will serve to fix a lower limit for the age of the earth, and this is found to be 4,500 million years.

Other radioactive decay chains have been used in similar experiments, e.g.

uranium-235 → lead-207 $(t_{\frac{1}{2}} = 7 \cdot 1 \times 10^8 \text{ y})$

thorium-232 → lead-208 $(t_{\frac{1}{2}} = 1 \cdot 39 \times 10^{10} \text{ y})$

potassium-40 → calcium-40 + argon-40 $(t_{\frac{1}{2}} = 1 \cdot 3 \times 10^9 \text{ y})$

rubidium-87 → strontium-87 $(t_{\frac{1}{2}} = 4 \cdot 3 \times 10^{10} \text{ y})$

In general they give similar results. The method has also been used to estimate the ages of meteorites, which turn out to be of the same order as that of the earth.

An isotope of shorter half-life, carbon-14 ($t_{\frac{1}{2}} = 5{,}600$ y, beta decay to the stable isotope, nitrogen-14) is used to measure time spans of the order of 600–40,000 years, which is the range of interest to archaeologists. In this instance, the values of N and N_0 must be replaced by the specific activities A and A_0, to give a modified decay equation:

$$A = A_0 \cdot e^{-\lambda t}$$

The value of A_0 follows from the fact that the carbon atoms in all living matter participate sooner or later in the natural 'carbon cycle' and come to have the same isotopic composition (mainly 12, some 13, traces of 14) as the carbon dioxide in the earth's atmosphere. In the atmosphere, nitrogen is transmuted into carbon-14 by bombardment with neutrons which are derived from the cosmic rays:

$$^{14}_{7}N + ^{1}_{0}n \rightarrow ^{14}_{6}C + ^{1}_{1}H$$

After 30,000 years (a long period compared with the half-life of carbon-14) the rate of decay of carbon-14 is exactly balanced by the rate of production from nitrogen, provided that the nature and flux of the cosmic ray bombardment and the content of nitrogen and of carbon dioxide in the atmosphere have remained constant. The carbon-14 method, introduced by W. L. Libby of the University of Chicago in 1949, is used for the 'dating' of those archaeological specimens which include carbon that was initially present in living plants or animals. The value of A_0 is then assumed to be equal to the specific activity of present-day carbon in the atmosphere or in living matter—this is approximately 15·3 disintegrations $\min^{-1} g^{-1}$ of carbon. The carbon-14 in dead matter receives no replenishment from the atmosphere by the 'carbon cycle', and it decays with a half-life of 5,600 years. A direct measurement on a sample of carbon dioxide or acetylene prepared from the archaeological specimen in the laboratory gives the present-day value of A. The modified decay equation may then be solved for t:

$$t = 1/\lambda \, \log_e \frac{A_0}{A}$$

The method has been tested on specimens of age up to 5,000 years which can be dated fairly precisely on other archaeological evidence, and it proves to be satisfactory within the limits of error of plus or minus 5–10 per cent. These errors are imposed by the experimental difficulties of exact measurement of very low specific activities of a low energy (0·158 MeV) beta emitter.

The radiocarbon method has been used to determine the previously unknown ages of various archaeological specimens, including such interesting examples as:

(a) The linen covering to the scroll of the Book of Isaiah (one of the Dead Sea Scrolls), dated 35 B.C. ± 200 years.

(b) Charcoal from the Lascaux cave (site of remarkable wall paintings) in the Dordogne district of France. Dated 14,000 B.C. ± 900 years.

(c) A charcoal sample from Stonehenge, dated 1846 B.C. ± 275 years.

ATOMIC LABELS

NON-ISOTOPIC LABELLING

A biologist who wishes to keep track of birds during migration might attach a coloured ring to the bird's leg: a civil engineer who was studying coastal erosion might deposit a few lorry loads of brightly painted pebbles on the beach in the hope of being able to follow their movement up or down the coast. These are examples of the labelling of objects in order to follow their subsequent movements, and this can often also be accomplished very conveniently with the aid of radioactive isotopes. There is usually no question of any chemical or isotopic identity between the label and the labelled object—the important technical problems are to secure firm adhesion of the label and to detect its radiations with ease. A good example is that of the labelling of pebbles with the isotope barium-140 ($t_{\frac{1}{2}} = 12\cdot8$ days) in equilibrium with its daughter product, lanthanum-140 ($t_{\frac{1}{2}} = 40\cdot2$ h). These isotopes emit penetrating gamma rays with a maximum energy of 2·9 MeV. The overall rate of radioactive decay is controlled by the half-life of the parent, barium-140. This half-life is long enough to permit useful experiments on the movement of pebbles by coastal currents but is not so long as to pose a hazard to public health. A few microcuries of the isotope is introduced into a small hole in the pebble, in the case of soft pebbles such as sandstones the hole is then sealed with a hard-setting resin. Flint pebbles are labelled by immersing them in a solution of the isotope, and then baking the wet pebbles. The activity adheres firmly to the surface of the flint pebble, even during subsequent exposure to rough weather.

A radioactive pebble can be detected amongst the other pebbles and sand on the beach, with a portable gamma scintillation counter, even when it is buried 6 in. beneath the surface. The pebble can also be detected on the bed of the sea, using a waterproofed detector lowered from a cable.

ISOTOPIC LABELLING—COMPLETE EXCHANGE

The use of radioactive isotopes discussed in the last section was as a marker or label to distinguish some particular material object, and was no different in principle from the use of paint, plastic rings or tags, etc.

A *unique* use of isotopes is that of labelling a particular chemical element or compound. One does not in practice label every single atom of the element in the specimen under examination. The sensitivity of detection of radioactivity is so high that only one out of every million or thousand million atoms need be a radioactive one. For example, the specific activity of carrier free phosphorus-32 ($t_{\frac{1}{2}} = 14 \cdot 5$ days) may be calculated as about 10^{12} disintegrations $\text{min}^{-1} \, \mu\text{g}^{-1}$. Since a properly shielded Geiger counter can easily measure 10^2 disintegrations min^{-1}, it follows that we can still measure one microgramme of isotopically labelled phosphorus, even when the ratio of phosphorus-32 to inactive phosphorus-31 is reduced to 1 part in 10^{10}. Another aspect of this high degree of sensitivity is that by increasing the proportion of labelled atoms as far as possible, one can often detect extremely small quantities of the element. In the case of phosphorus-32, the value quoted for the specific activity of carrier-free material sold by the Amersham establishment of the U.K.A.E.A. is 'greater than 1,000 c/g of phosphorus', i.e. *greater than* 2×10^9 disintegrations $\text{min}^{-1} \, \mu\text{g}^{-1}$. In practice the presence of traces of inactive phosphorus as impurity in water, reagents, vessels, etc., always sets some limit lower than the theoretical specific activity of 10^{12} disintegrations $\text{min}^{-1} \, \mu\text{g}^{-1}$. Accepting a value of 10^9, and noting that we can easily measure 10^2, we may calculate the limit of sensitivity of measuring the element phosphorus, when labelled in this way, as $1 \, \mu\text{g} \times \dfrac{10^2}{10^9}$ $= 10^{-13}$ g. This great sensitivity makes it possible to follow the chemical properties of elements and compounds in extremely dilute solution. For example, one can determine the degree of solubility of very sparingly soluble compounds such as metallic sulphides, and one can (using special techniques of detecting radio-activity in the vapour phase) measure very low vapour pressures of substances which one would usually class as non-volatile, e.g. white phosphorus ($0 \cdot 0044$ mm at $0°$ C, $0 \cdot 029$ mm at $21°$ C).

The applications described above involve the insertion of a relatively small number of radioactively labelled atoms, uniformly dispersed amongst the normal atoms of a particular element. The labelled atoms are taken from some relatively concentrated preparation, supplied by an Atomic Energy Laboratory such as that at Amersham. In many cases the radioactive isotope has been prepared by the neutron irradiation of the inactive element in a nuclear reactor, e.g.

$$_{15}^{31}P + _{0}^{1}n \rightarrow _{15}^{32}P \text{ (beta emitter, } t_{\frac{1}{2}} = 14 \cdot 5 \text{ d)}$$

or, for preparations of high specific activity:

$$_{16}^{32}S + _{0}^{1}n \rightarrow _{15}^{32}P + _{1}^{1}H$$

An alternative approach to the measurement of a very small quantity of inactive phosphorus would be to take the sample to a nuclear reactor and there to irradiate it with neutrons, so that a fraction of the phosphorus atoms in the sample became radioactive. After removing the sample from the exposure to neutrons, the radioactivity due to phosphorus-32 could be measured, either directly on the sample, or after some chemical separation of the phosphorus in order to free it from other radioactive isotopes which may be present as impurities. The number of disintegrations per unit time, due to radioactive phosphorus, is proportional to the total weight of inactive phosphorus in the sample which was irradiated. This is the basis of the important technique of 'radioactivation analysis' which is now used widely for the quantitative measurement of trace elements in semiconductors and other 'superpure' industrial materials, in minerals and meteorites, in plants, water and foodstuffs, etc., and also on an increasing scale for the rapid and *non-destructive* analysis of the elements which are present as major components in various industrial materials or in museum specimens (the method was applied at Oxford in 1960 to the non-destructive analysis of several hundred Greek coins of the 5th century B.C.).

In detail, the method consists of irradiating a weighed quantity (0·1 to 1g) of the unknown sample, together with a suitable standard which contains a known weight of the element which has been selected for analysis. The irradiation is usually carried out for at least one half-life of the isotope which is produced (14 days in the case of phosphorus). Analysts who do not work at the site of a nuclear reactor can send their samples for irradiation to the Isotope

Division at A.E.R.E., Harwell, or to similar establishments in other countries. It is often possible to irradiate several samples and a standard, each sealed in a polythene capsule, within one screw stoppered aluminium can which measures 1 in. diameter by 2 in. long and which is the normal unit for such irradiations in the BEPO reactor at Harwell. A neutron flux of 10^{11} to 10^{12} neutrons $cm^{-2} sec^{-1}$ is available in BEPO.

The growth of radioactivity due to the desired element in the sample follows the equation derived in Chapter 8:

$$\lambda_B \cdot n_B = n_a \cdot \sigma \cdot f(1 - e^{-\lambda_B \cdot t})$$

The worked example on p. 100 shows that the irradiation of 10^{-6} g of arsenic for 14 h at a flux of 10^{12} neutrons $cm^{-2} sec^{-1}$ produces $6 \cdot 2 \times 10^5$ disintegrations min^{-1} of arsenic-76 ($t_{\frac{1}{2}} = 26 \cdot 7$ h).

A similar quantity of phosphorus, irradiated for 14 days, would produce $1 \cdot 2 \times 10^5$ disintegrations min^{-1} of phosphorus-32 ($t_{\frac{1}{2}} = 14 \cdot 5$ days). Remembering that we can conveniently measure as little as 10^2 disintegrations min^{-1} of a beta emitter such as arsenic-76 or phosphorus-32, it is obvious that radioactivation analysis is potentially capable of the quantitative determination of as little as $10^{-6} \times 10^2/6 \cdot 2 \times 10^5$ or about 10^{-10} g of arsenic in the sample taken for analysis. The sensitivity depends upon the activation cross-section for the isotope in question, and upon the neutron flux. Of the 103 known elements, 21 are naturally radioactive and their radioactivity can be measured with great sensitivity without any need for activation. Seventy out of the remaining 82 stable elements can be analysed by the simple method of radioactivation analysis which we have discussed, with ultimate sensitivities which range from 10^{-6} to 10^{-12} g. Many of the remaining 12 elements can be determined by a modified method of radioactivation.

To attain the high sensitivities quoted above, we cannot simply remove the irradiated sample from the nuclear reactor and measure the radioactivity forthwith. The radioactivity due to the required isotope—say, arsenic-76—may be swamped by extraneous radioactivity due to other constituents. For example, in the analysis of traces of arsenic in blood, it has been calculated that the irradiation of 10^{-6} g of arsenic in 1 ml of blood for 5 days would yield, not only 2×10^6 dis. min^{-1} of arsenic-76, but also 4×10^7 dis. min^{-1} of chlorine-38 (half-life, 37 min) and 2×10^8 dis. min^{-1} of sodium-24 (half-life, $14 \cdot 8$ h). Rather than undertake the labour of the quantitative separation and purification of 10^{-6} g of arsenic, with the attendant risks of losses such as those due to absorption on precipitates, the analyst adds 50 mg of inactive arsenic as a 'carrier' for the arsenic-76. Provided that the mixture can now be treated so as to bring all arsenic atoms, normal and radioactive, into the same chemical form—say as arsenate—the subsequent chemistry need not be quantitative. The problem of the quantitative recovery of 10^{-6} g of arsenic (or it could well be 10^{-10} g, for radioactivation analysis has been applied at this low level) is replaced by that of purifying 50 mg of arsenic, with a careful determination of the chemical yield, that is, the percentage recovery of the added arsenic carrier. In the specific sample of the determination of arsenic in biological material, the arsenic in the sample might be present as AsO_2^{1-}, AsO_3^{3-}, AsO_4^{3-}, As^{3+}, or as an organic compound. The carrier is added as sodium arsenate, followed by the wet oxidation of the sample and the carrier with hydrogen peroxide, nitric acid, sulphuric acid and perchloric acid. The radiochemical purification of the arsenic activity, in the presence of the carrier, involves normal chemical procedures such as precipitation, distillation, solvent extraction, ion exchange and chromatography. The purification of arsenic in irradiated biological material includes several precipitations as the metal with ammonium hypophosphite, distillation under oxidizing conditions to remove impurities such as germanium while the arsenic remains in the acid mixture, and distillation of arsenic as arsenious chloride under reducing conditions. The arsenic carrier is finally precipitated as the metal, weighed and transferred to a small aluminium 'counting tray' for the measurement of beta activity with a Geiger counter. Much of the reliability of radioactivation analysis arises from the checks which can be made upon the identity and the purity of the arsenic-76 (or other isotope as appropriate).

(a) In the first instance, the radiochemical purity of the final precipitates, which have been isolated from the sample and from the standard, may be checked by a series of decay measurements. After appropriate corrections, the count rates at various intervals are plotted on a logarithmic scale against time on a linear scale. Successive count rates obtained during the decay of a single radiochemically pure isotope will lie on a straight line of slope related to the half-life (see Chapter 5).

(b) Alternatively, the penetrating power of the beta radiation may be measured through a series of aluminium absorbers of increasing thickness, with correction for any concomitant decay. The corrected count rates are plotted on a logarithmic scale, against the absorber thickness on a linear scale. The shape of the absorption curve is characteristic of the beta spectrum of a particular isotope and may be closely compared with standard curves recorded with especially purified isotopes under the same conditions. The penetrating power of any gamma radiation emitted by the isolated radioactive isotope may be measured through a series of lead absorbers: a scintillation counter would normally be used as a detector.

(c) Finally, the characteristic gamma spectrum of the isotope can be recorded by means of a sodium iodide scintillation spectrometer. The record may be compared with standards.

It is not expected that all the three parameters, half-life, shape of beta absorption curve and shape of gamma spectrometer record, can in each case be precisely determined. In general, enough characteristic results may be gathered to establish the required degree of purity.

In certain favourable cases, radioactivation analysis does not require the relatively high neutron flux found in a nuclear reactor, and it is possible to use laboratory neutron sources (e.g. a mixture of antimony-124, polonium-210 or plutonium-239 with powdered beryllium) which give 10^3–10^4 neutrons $cm^{-2} sec^{-1}$ from the reactions:

$$\ce{^4_2He} + \ce{^9_4Be} \rightarrow \ce{^{12}_6C} + \ce{^1_0n}$$

or
$$h\nu + \ce{^9_4Be} \rightarrow 2\ce{^4_2He} + \ce{^1_0n}$$

or a van der Graaf generator which supplies 2 or 3 MeV deuterons for the bombardment of a beryllium target and gives 10^9 neutrons $cm^{-2} sec^{-1}$ from the reaction:

$$\ce{^2_1H} + \ce{^9_4Be} \rightarrow \ce{^{10}_5B} + \ce{^1_0n}$$

ISOTOPIC LABELLING—INCOMPLETE EXCHANGE

A unique use of radioactive isotopes is to label only a particular fraction of the atoms of an element, and then to use them to follow chemical and physical rearrangements. A classical example is the study of self-diffusion, for example of copper atoms within metallic copper.

A thin sheet of metallic copper is made radioactive by neutron irradiation:

$$\ce{^{63}_{29}Cu} + \ce{^1_0n} \rightarrow \ce{^{64}_{29}Cu} \quad (t_{\frac{1}{2}} = 12\cdot 8\ \text{h})$$

$$\ce{^{64}_{29}Cu} \begin{cases} \xrightarrow{\beta-} \ce{^{64}_{30}Zn} \\ \xrightarrow{\beta+} \ce{^{64}_{28}Ni} \end{cases} \text{stable isotopes}$$

165

(The copper-64 decays both by beta decay to zinc *and* by positron decay to nickel. Both the beta particle and the positron can be detected by a Geiger counter.)

The radioactive sheet of copper is now clamped firmly against a normal block of copper, the faces which are in contact having been very accurately machined to be parallel. In the course of time, atoms of the tracer isotope, copper-64, diffuse into the un-irradiated block (and, of course, atoms of the inactive isotopes, copper-63 and copper-65, diffuse into the irradiated sheet). The rate of diffusion may be calculated from measurements of the specific activity of samples of metal taken from the unirradiated block at various distances from the junction.

If c is the concentration of copper-64, l the distance from the interface and t the time that has elapsed, then Fick's Law of Diffusion states that:

$$dc/dt = D \cdot d^2c/dl^2$$

where D is the diffusion coefficient. The values of D for copper are: $1 \cdot 15 \times 10^{-8}$ cm^2 h^{-1} at 650° C, rising to $1 \cdot 01 \times 10^{-5}$ at 1030° C (m.p. = 1083° C).

An even more important use of radioactive isotopes is to label particular atoms in a complicated molecule or to trace the behaviour of compounds through intricate biological processes. This application depends on the lack of complete exchange between all the atoms of, say, carbon in an organic chemical, because the valency bonds are not easily broken. For example, the compound phenyl glyoxal may be obtained with the keto-carboxyl group labelled with carbon-14 (shown by an asterisk in the diagram below)

$$C_6H_5 - \overset{*}{C} - C - H \quad \text{(Phenyl glyoxal)}$$
$$\qquad\ \ \| \quad \|$$
$$\qquad\ \ O \quad O$$

At least 200 different labelled compounds of carbon-14 are available from stock at the Radiochemical Centre, Amersham, Bucks. These compounds are synthesized by standard reactions from intermediates which are derived from labelled barium carbonate, $Ba\overset{*}{C}O_3$. A knowledge of the mechanism of these standard reactions makes it possible to affirm that the final compound is labelled at some specific site, such as the ketonic carbon atom in phenyl glyoxal. This particular compound, for example, might possibly be prepared in the following steps:

166

$$Ba\overset{*}{C}O_3 + 2HCl = BaCl_2 + H_2O + \overset{*}{C}O_2$$

$\overset{*}{C}O_2 + C_6H_5MgBr$ (phenyl magnesium bromide, a Grignard reagent)

$$= C_6H_5\overset{*}{\underset{\overset{\|}{O}}{C}}{-}OMgBr$$

$C_6H_5\overset{*}{\underset{\overset{\|}{O}}{C}}{-}OMgBr + H{-}\underset{\overset{\|}{O}}{C}{-}H$ (formaldehyde)

$$= C_6H_5{-}\underset{\overset{\|}{O}}{\overset{*}{C}}{-}\underset{\overset{\|}{O}}{C}{-}H + Mg(OH)Br$$

The labelled compound may be used to decide between two or more possible reaction mechanisms, e.g. in the conversion of phenyl glyoxal to the anion of mandelic acid $(C_6H_5CHOH\cdot CO_2)^-$ by the action of hydroxyl ion. The hydroxyl ion may attack either of the two carbon atoms in the side chain:

First possibility

Second possibility

The decision between these alternative mechanisms depends upon knowing the position of the labelled carbon atom in the mandelic acid which is produced. Mandelic acid is readily oxidized to benzoic acid and carbon dioxide on heating with potassium dichromate and sulphuric acid:

$$C_6H_5CHOH \cdot CO_2H + 2[O] = C_6H_5CO_2H + CO_2 + H_2O$$

This provides a method for testing the radioactivity associated with (*a*) the carbon atom nearest the phenyl group, by measurement of the benzoic acid, and (*b*) the carbon atom remote from the phenyl group, by measurement of the carbon dioxide which is evolved. Experimentally, it was found by Neville in 1948 that the labelled carbon was in the benzoic acid and not in the carbon dioxide—that is, the second mechanism for the conversion of phenyl glyoxal to mandelic acid is the correct one.

The use of isotopic tracers in this way has thrown much light upon the mechanism of organic reactions and upon biological processes. For example, it has been shown that the 'steady state' of many biochemical systems is the result of a dynamic equilibrium. Many of the cells of our bodily organs, for example, are continually being replaced by new ones and the same is true of the chemical molecules in the blood and other body fluids. Both radioactive and stable isotopic tracers have been used in these researches—the stable isotopes include oxygen-18, deuterium and carbon-13, the specific activity of which can be measured by mass spectrometry or in the case of deuterium or oxygen-18 by accurate measurements of the density of water. The advantage of radioactive tracers such as carbon-14 and tritium (hydrogen-3) often lies in the extreme sensitivity of their measurement.

12

THE BIOLOGICAL EFFECTS OF RADIOACTIVITY

INTRODUCTION

The earliest recognition of the biological effects of radioactivity was by the German scientists Walkhoff and Giesel in 1900. The effect was also noted by Pierre Curie, who exposed his arm to the action of radium and recorded the progress of healing of the burn, and Henri Becquerel, who suffered a burn from a phial of radium he was carrying in his waistcoat pocket.

Papers published by Curie and Becquerel led French doctors to examine the effect of radium on tumours. Before long, radium was being used in hospitals for the treatment of cancer, and factories were set up in France and the U.S.A., from about 1903, to prepare this valuable substance. Unfortunately, the dangerous properties of radioactivity and X-rays were not immediately understood, and many of the early scientific and medical workers died of cancer and other diseases caused by the radiation. A memorial at Hamburg commemorates 169 radiologists who eventually died of illnesses which were induced by over-exposure to X-rays. Again, many young women who were employed to apply luminous paint, which contained radium, to watch and clock dials, subsequently died of cancer. They had been accustomed to moisten with their lips, the small paint brushes, and in this way traces of radium had entered their bodies.

In one sense we have benefited from these early tragedies, in that the need for a strict control of radioactive materials had become understood—by bitter experience—before the discovery of nuclear fission in 1939. The peaceful uses of radioactive isotopes and of nuclear power, on a scale far greater than the pre-war use of X-rays and radium, do not now produce injury to the operators, for we understand the dangers and we insist upon necessary precautions—which are in fact now required by law. The military use of nuclear bombs, as at Hiroshima and Nagasaki in 1945, not only involves a great increase in the explosive power of weapons, but also presents unprecedented biological consequences due to the instantaneous gamma rays and neutrons and to the more persistent radioactive fission products. Some of the consequences are not limited to the population in the immediate locality of the detonation. 'Radioactive fallout' may affect distant parts of the globe, and also the genetic effects (p. 176) may cause diseases in subsequent generations.

In peace and in war, radioactivity is now an important and permanent factor in world affairs, and it is well that all citizens should have some understanding of its biological effects. In the next section, we will try to understand the scientific principles which govern the interaction of radioactive substances and X-rays with living matter.

INTERACTION OF RADIATION WITH LIVING MATTER

We have already mentioned several special features of the interaction of radiation with living matter, and these are summarized below:

(a) It can cause burns, and in other ways damage or destroy living tissue. Basically, radiation is destructive.

(b) It can act from *outside* the body, e.g. the radiologists who suffered from over-exposure to the body (X-rays), or from *inside* the body, e.g. the radium which was swallowed by the painters of luminous dials.

(c) It can destroy cancerous growth but can also cause cancer.

(d) It can have a delayed effect.

The first two features can be dealt with up to a point, in terms of the physical properties of alpha, beta and gamma radiations, which we have already discussed in the earlier chapters of this book. The last two features require some consideration of the detailed physical, chemical and physiological mechanisms by which radiation may act on individual living cells and on the entire body.

PHYSICAL ASPECTS

In one sense, the interaction of radioactive substances with living matter can be treated as a transfer of energy. Alpha and beta particles and gamma rays can transfer part or all of their energy during their passage through matter, one example of which is the ionization of air or of other gases, as in the cloud chamber and the Geiger counter. The loss of energy due to ionization and to other inelastic collisions with atoms of the air or of some other absorbing material, means that eventually an alpha or a beta particle comes to rest within the absorber, for it has a maximum range at which all its kinetic energy is expended. The loss of energy from gamma rays (or

X-rays) follows a rather different mechanism (Chapter 4), so that we do not speak of a maximum range of a gamma ray but rather of a 'half-thickness'. Typical values for the maximum ranges of alpha and beta particles and of the half-thicknesses for gamma rays have been quoted in Chapters 1–4 for absorbers such as air, water and metals. Living tissue will also act as an absorber, because it contains atoms of carbon, hydrogen, oxygen, nitrogen, etc., and typical values are quoted in Table 12.1.

Table 12.1. Absorption of Radiation in Living Tissue

Radiation	Energy (MeV)	Maximum range (cm)	Half-thickness (cm)
Alpha	4	0·007	—
Beta	0·5	0·15	—
Gamma	3	—	28

Two important points emerge from Table 12.1. First, the alpha particle loses its kinetic energy and is brought to rest within a very thin layer of tissue. Alpha particles from a radioactive source outside the human body, for example, are not able to penetrate the skin and so cannot directly produce internal injuries. On the other hand, if a radioactive substance is accidentally taken *into* the human body—by inhalation or swallowing or through an open cut or other wound—any alpha particles it emits will harmfully expend *all* their kinetic energy inside the body. Second, the behaviour of gamma rays is rather different, for rays which proceed from an external source can penetrate the skin and other body surfaces (this is, after all, what happens during an X-ray photograph). Gamma rays emitted *inside* the body will lose some but not all of their energy within the body and in this respect are less harmful than internal alpha sources of similar energy. Beta particles occupy a position intermediate between alpha particles and gamma rays.

A practical significance of the elementary physical facts contained in Table 12.1 and discussed above is that the harmful effects of radioactive substances upon the human body fall into two classes:

(1) External radiation—the greatest danger being from gamma rays (or X-rays). It was this hazard that claimed 169 radiologists as victims (p. 169).

(2) Internal radiation—the greatest danger being from alpha (e.g. radium, plutonium) and to a lesser degree from beta emitters

(e.g. strontium-90). It was this hazard that claimed victims from the radium painters (p. 169).

We have based our discussion thus far upon the physical fact that energy can be transferred from alpha and beta particles or gamma rays and X-rays to such biological material as the tissue of the human body. It is necessary to define certain units with which one can measure the exact amount of energy which is transferred in this way.

The roentgen absorbed dose ('rad') is the unit which measures the amount of energy which is released within any absorbing material (air, water, tissue, etc.) due to the passage of ionizing radiation. One rad is defined as 100 ergs per gramme. The transfer of energy from radiation to some portion of the human body may produce harmful biological effects to an extent which depends not only on the total amount of energy transferred, but also upon the nature of the radiation—whether alpha, beta, gamma, X-ray, slow or fast neutrons. One reason for this difference of 'Relative Biological Efficiency' (R.B.E.) of the various types of radiation lies in the differing pattern of ionization which they produce.

Typical values for the R.B.E. are:

Gamma or X-rays	1
Beta	1
Alpha	10–20
Thermal neutrons	5
Fast neutrons	10

It is sometimes convenient to multiply the total energy deposition, measured in rads, by the R.B.E. to give a unit called the 'rem' (roentgen equivalent man) which is defined as 'the quantity of radiation which produces the same biological damage in man as that resulting from the absorption of 1 rad of X-rays or gamma rays.'

Some idea of the scale of these units (rem) may be obtained from the following facts:

(a) The 'background' radiation of the human body due to cosmic rays, potassium-40, carbon-14 and traces of radium and other naturally occurring alpha emitters, etc., is about 0·1 rem per year.

(b) The recommended maximum limit of whole body radiation due to the handling of radioactive isotopes, X-ray machines, nuclear reactors, etc., for workers selected as medically fit for such exposure, is 5 rem per year.

(c) The estimated value of the LD^{50} for the whole body irradiation of human beings is 500 rem, delivered over a short period of

172

up to 4 h. (LD^{50} is the dose at which 50 per cent of the exposed population would die within a month.)

It will be noted that we have quoted not the total energy in 'rem', but what is called the 'dose rate' in 'rem per unit time'. This is meant to imply that the biological effects usually depend on the duration of the period during which the radiation is applied. Some biological effects of radiation (e.g. the mutation of genes) are irreversible and depend only upon the total dose, but in many others, including radiation sickness in animals and humans, a certain degree of recovery from small doses is possible. For example, a dose of 200 rem whole body radiation is acceptable to the International Commission on Radiological Protection for occupationally exposed workers, if spread over a working lifetime, so that at any stage the interim dose does not exceed $5(N - 18)$ rem, where N is the age in years. By contrast, a dose of 200 rem whole body radiation delivered over a short period (as in a nuclear explosion) would probably cause serious illness, including nausea, diarrhoea and vomiting within 24 h and a possibility (about 1 in 20) of death within 30 days. Doses of several thousand rem may be safely delivered to selected parts of the human body during radiotherapy for malignant and non-malignant diseases, e.g. tumours, warts, veruccas, provided that most of the body is shielded.

BIOLOGICAL ASPECTS

We have several times used the phrase 'whole body radiation'. It is important to realize that the various organs and limbs of the body vary greatly in their response to radiation, and this is also true of the response of different animals and micro-organisms. For humans, the bones, nerves and muscles are relatively *resistant* and the lymphatic tissue and bone marrow are relatively *susceptible* to radiation. This susceptibility shows itself in a decrease in the level of white blood cells in the blood (leucopenia) and later of red blood cells (anaemia). A long-term result may be leukaemia, which is an uncontrolled over-production of the white blood-cells.

The decrease in the resistance of organisms from simple unicellular organisms to mammals is shown by the values of the lethal dose, LD^{50} in Table 12.2.

Not only do different organisms vary in their susceptibility to radiation, but so does the individual cell at various phases of its life history. In asexual reproduction, the cells divide by the process of mitosis, which consists of successive phases: resting phase, prophase, metaphase, anaphase, telophase, resting phase. Radiation is more destructive during the resting phase and the early part of the prophase.

One result of a high dose of radiation, administered during the resting phase or early prophase, is that the chromosomes which become visible under the microscope at the metaphase are seen to have breaks and irregular linkages.

Obviously the effect of radiation on living matter is more complicated than simply the deposition of a given quantity of energy, or the production of a given amount of ionization, within a certain

Table 12.2. Approximate Values of LD^{50} for Various Organisms

Organism	LD^{50} (rem)
Paramecia	300,000
B. coli	10,000
Mammals	200–1000
Man	500

weight of live material. We have seen that the biological results depend not only on the total dose in rems, but upon such factors as:

(1) The time scale. On the one hand, the effect of a given total dose may be minimized if it is administered so slowly that recovery mechanisms can keep pace with the damage. On the other hand, some effects are long-term and may appear several years after the dose has ceased.

(2) The variation in the sensitivity of various organisms and of the various types of differentiated tissue, organs, etc., of the body.

(3) The variation in the sensitivity of a given type of living cell at various phases in its life cycle.

BIOLOGICAL MECHANISMS

Living material is not simply a passive absorber of energy, in which the kinetic energy of alpha or beta particles or the quantum energy of gamma or X-rays may be changed to thermal energy and ionization energy. It is a complicated biochemical and physiological system and it is hardly surprising that the brutal injection of large quantities of energy from a foreign source produces malfunction and even death. The exact mechanism of the disturbance is still not completely understood. 'The concensus of opinion is that radiation acts primarily upon the cell and its constituents, and upon the complex chemical processes occurring in these, rather

174

than upon the fluids in which the cell is bathed. It is thought that the processes associated with the formation of ions during the passage of radiation lead to changes in some of the highly organized molecular systems within the cell.'*

There are at least two ways in which ionizing radiation could affect the 'highly organized molecular systems':

The direct or 'target' theory—This was particularly developed by D. E. Lea at Cambridge during the 1940's. Ionization may occur very near or within a giant molecule of protein, nucleic acid, etc., leading to a disruption of certain valency bonds. This approach finds some support in the experimental fact that the chromosomes in living cells are often found to be broken or reunited in abnormal patterns following exposure to radiation. One could suppose that the ionizing radiation had cut a deadly path through a chromosome which lay across its track. Lea calculated that 700 eV of energy would be sufficient to break a chromosome in the living cell. The effectiveness of an ionizing radiation would then depend upon the ionization density along its track, hence the high R.B.E. for alpha particles. The invisible ionization track in the wake of the particle might, of course, break up other molecules within the cell—a unique feature of the chromosomes in particular is that they can be stained with special dyes and are then visible under the microscope, when their string-like appearance makes it easy to detect breaks.

The indirect or 'chemical' theory—Three facts make it likely that the direct theory is too crude.

First, the extent of chromosome damage in irradiated cells depends upon the partial pressure of oxygen in the gaseous atmosphere with which they are in contact. In replacing normal air by pure nitrogen, the number of chromosome breakages is reduced by a factor of three.

Second, the passage of ionizing radiation through an aqueous solution (the cell fluid may be regarded as such) has been shown to produce reactive chemical species such as the free radicals H, HO and HO_2. The partial pressure of oxygen would affect the concentration of these species. It has further been shown that any enzymes and other giant molecules dissolved in the solution are attacked by the reactive radicals, to produce marked changes in their chemical composition. A limited degree of protection of mice against death by radiation is conferred by the prior administration of inhibitors such as β-mercaptoethylamine, $NH_2CH_2CH_2SH$.

* *The Hazards to Man of Nuclear and Allied Radiations*, Medical Research Council, Cmd. 9780, H.M.S.O., 1956, p. 7.

The inhibitors apparently serve to bear the brunt of the chemical attack by the free radicals, for they may be shown to suppress free radicals in aqueous solutions in the laboratory.

Third, it is now known that not only radiation, but also an assorted group of chemicals, including mustard gas $S(CH_2CH_2Cl)_2$ have the property of damaging the chromosomes. These include substances used as 'cross-linking' agents in the field of textile fibres and in general the group are called 'radiomimetic agents'.

To sum up, the passage of radiation through a living cell leads to changes in some of the highly organized molecular systems within the cell. These include breaks in the chromosomes as well as elusive injuries (to the chromosomes and to other components of the cell) which cannot be seen under the microscope. 'These changes are probably brought about by highly reactive chemical intermediates liberated within the cell subsequent to the physical process of ionization' (Medical Research Council, as quoted on p.1 75).

GENETIC EFFECTS OF RADIATION

The effect of chromosome damage during irradiation leads us to expect the possibility of damage or alteration in the genes. These are the sub-microscopic factors which govern the transmission of inherited characteristics (eye colour, hair colour, baldness, etc.) and which are usually supposed to lie at intervals along the length of the chromosome (several thousand different genes along a chromosome from the human species). In fact, H. J. Muller in the United States discovered in 1927 that the rate of appearance of gene mutations in *Drosophila melanogaster*, the fruit fly, could be increased by exposure to X-rays. Subsequent work has confirmed this for a wide range of plants, insects and animals, and radiation has been used by plant breeders to produce mutations in the seeds of fruits, vegetables and grain, instead of waiting upon the slow rate of 'natural mutation'. It must be explained that occasionally a gene appears to change suddenly, for a single plant or animal appears which is a 'sport'—that is, it shows some abnormal characteristic, e.g. wheat with an abnormally thick stalk. If this characteristic can be passed on to subsequent generations, it is ascribed to a 'natural mutation' of a gene. A large part of the work of the plant breeder is to select one or two natural mutations out of thousands which show promise of some agricultural advantage, and then to multiply the modified seed stock by breeding. It must be emphasized that *most* mutations are harmful. Natural selection has in the process of time retained the more useful inherited characteristics, and

this process has been further refined by the plant breeders themselves in their choice of promising lines taken from the opportunities
presented by spontaneous mutations.

As most genes on the chromosome of any particular variety
of wheat will be ones representing favourable characteristics, it is
likely that any additional mutation in one of the genes will spoil
rather than improve the agricultural performance of the wheat.
The plant breeder is looking for the one exceptional case where the
change is for the better, and he is ruthless in discarding most of the
plants he grows in his experimental plots from seed which has been
subject to gene mutation. In a sense he is gambling in a lottery.
Radiation comes to his aid by increasing the number of tickets
he holds.

Three factors must now be introduced which make the above
discussion of gene mutation of extreme concern to the human race.

(a) The increase of mutation rate by exposure to radiation must
be assumed to apply to humans. 'Since the genetic mechanism
in man is the same as that in other animal and plant species and
since the animals and plants that have been studied all show the
same type of genetic response to ionizing radiations, it would be
unreasonable to suppose that the response in man will do other
than follow the same general pattern' (Medical Research Council
Report, 1956). In practice this would mean an increase in the
number of people who suffer from such known genetically transmitted diseases as achondroplasia (dwarfism), haemophilia,
muscular dystrophy, albinism, total colour blindness and phenyl-
ketonuria. Research work with plants and animals shows that an
increased *rate* of mutation does not introduce completely new *types*
of mutations: the diseases listed above are examples of those which
arise by natural mutation even in the absence of additional radiation.

(b) The dose of radiation required to change significantly the
spontaneous mutation rate is rather low (much lower than the lowest
dose which produces clinical symptoms in any exposed individual).

Estimates of the dose to double the natural rate in man vary
from 15 to 80 rads, delivered to the gonads during the years up
to parenthood (the extent of these years may be estimated from
the statistical average age of reproduction which in 1956 was
28 years for women, 32 years for men). Supposing that the 'doubling
dose' of 15 to 80 rads is spread out over 10 to 14 years, say from
age 18 until parenthood, the dose rate is only 1 to 8 rads per year,
which is not much higher than the average dose rates quoted for
atomic energy, medical and industrial workers in 1959 (0·4 rad
for 16,000 employees of the United Kingdom Atomic Energy

Authority, 0·6 rad for 11,000 other medical and industrial workers who were checked by the Radiological Protection Service). At these very low dose rates, no radiation illness has been observed amongst the workers, who receive periodic blood counts and other careful medical checks. Yet the increased radiation they receive, over and above the natural background of about 0·1 rem per year, must cause an increased number of mutations, for there are no grounds for believing that there is a threshold dose, below which *no* increase of mutation occurs.

(*c*) The human race, unlike the plant breeder, cannot murder thousands of abnormal offspring and select for care and attention a single improved child, if such a one was found. Many of the genetically transmitted diseases lower the unfortunate person's state of health including in some cases his mental abilities, but leave him or her the power of sexual reproduction. This means that, especially in a society where good medical services prolong the lives of the partially sick, the deleterious gene mutations are incompletely subject to the process of 'natural selection', and the mutations may be transmitted through a large number of subsequent generations.

In fact, many of the mutations are 'recessive', that is, they will not show up as a weakness (total colour blindness, and albinism are examples) until a child is born to a couple *each* of whom have inherited this particular gene mutation. Under these conditions, what becomes of importance is the increased mutation rate, averaged over a whole population or similar group within which marriage partners are usually selected. For example, the ordinary risk that a child of any given pair of parents will suffer a congenital mental defect (commonly called an imbecile or an idiot) is about 1 in 500. The risk for a given pair of parents, *both* of whom have suffered a doubling in the mutation rate before the conception of the child, is 1 in 485 (or 1 in 493 if only *one* parent had a doubled mutation rate). The risk of certain rare 'dominant' or 'sex-linked' genetic abnormalities would increase by a higher percentage, but at most this would mean doubling a remote chance, for example at present a 'natural' chance of 1 in 10,000 of achondroplasia (dwarfism) would increase to 1 in 5,000.

The Medical Research Council Report in 1956 concluded that 'For levels of radiation up to the doubling dose, and even some way beyond, the genetic effects of radiation are only appreciable when reckoned over the population as a whole and need cause no alarm to the individual on his own account . . .. For the offspring of any given parents the risk from increasing the mutation rate is very slight . . . it is only if members of an irradiated group or their descendants intermarry over several generations, and do not marry with the unirradiated population, that there is likely to be a disproportionately greater manifestation of hereditary defects among the descendants. Such an extreme degree of in-breeding is unlikely to occur. A fraction of the community can, therefore, without significant genetic risk to their progeny or harm to the population as a whole, receive doses of radiation which would be likely to have serious effects if applied to the whole population.'

The *averaged* genetically effective dose to the gonads of the population of Great Britain (allowing for the different age ranges) from man-made sources including occupational exposure, medical X-rays, fall-out from the testing of nuclear weapons, etc., has been calculated as about 23 per cent of that already received from the natural background (Table 12.3).

Table 12.3. Dose Rates to the Population from Natural Background and Man-made Sources

Source of radiation	Dose rate as percentage of natural background	Date of Calculation
Natural background (0·1 rad per year)	100	
Diagnostic radiology	19	1957
Shoe-fitting machines	0·1	1956
Luminous clocks and watches	1	1956
Occupational exposure, total (Medical, industry, U.K.A.E.A.)	0·5	1959
Fall-out from nuclear explosions (average 1955–9)	2·4	1955–9

PROTECTION AGAINST RADIATION

WHAT IS THE NORMAL?

No one has ever known *absolute* protection against radiation. Cosmic radiation bombards us from space. Traces of uranium, radium and thorium in rocks, soil and building materials give off alpha, beta and gamma radiation as well as the radioactive gas, radon. The natural radioactive impurities become incorporated into foodstuffs. Even if we could escape these external agents, our bodies themselves contain the elements potassium and carbon, which are feebly radioactive. The natural background of radiation varies with the latitude and longitude, height above sea level, the nature of the diet and the geology of the area (e.g. granite is more radioactive than chalk). An average figure of about 0·1 rem per year is commonly quoted for the British Isles.

A new and important branch of Industrial Hygiene is that of 'radiation protection', which aims at avoiding any significant increase above the natural background of radiation. The word 'significant' usually in practice implies a factor of about 2 for the general population, and about 50 for a restricted class of workers. The principles of radiation protection are important to all those who work with X-rays or radioactive sources in laboratories, hospitals, atomic energy factories, nuclear power stations, etc., and are, further, a potential concern to all citizens because of the possibility of accidents in nuclear plants, of fall-out from weapons tests and above all the use of nuclear weapons in war. The following discussion relates mainly to the precautions used in laboratories and factories. Civil Defence is mainly outside the scope of this textbook. Certain codes of practice and government memoranda have been promulgated, which should be consulted by any who are thinking of introducing work with radioactivity into a laboratory or factory. In Great Britain, the chief codes are:

Code of Practice for the Protection of Persons exposed to Ionizing Radiations, H.M. Stationery Office, 1957 (Hospital and medical uses).

Precautions in the use of Ionizing Radiation in Industry, H.M. Stationery Office, 1957.

The use of Radioactive Substances, X-rays and Gamma rays in Technical Colleges (Ministry of Education, Administration Memorandum 547, 29 March 1957).

The use of Radioactive Substances and X-ray Equipment in Schools (Ministry of Education, Administration Memorandum 577, 24 October 1958).

PROTECTION

There is at present no direct protection (e.g. an immunization) against radiation. What one has to do is *avoid* the radiation by any or all of the following expedients: (*a*) keep away, (*b*) be quick, (*c*) shield it, (*d*) keep it out.

(*a*) *Keep away*—The intensity of radiation diminishes with the square of the distance from the source. A radioactive source, even at 'tracer' levels of a few microcuries, should be handled with tongs or by long tweezers, to reduce the dose to the finger tips. More active sources, at the millicurie level, require special remote handling tongs, or 'easy reachers' of the type used by shop window-dressers, in order to reduce the dose of radiation to the whole body. Ingenious contrivances of levers, string and pulleys, geared rods, etc., can sometimes be erected in order to handle radioactive sources by 'remote control'.

(*b*) *Be quick*—For moderate dose rates at least, it is the *total integrated dose* that is the factor of biological importance. This can be limited by curtailing the time taken for the operation, e.g.

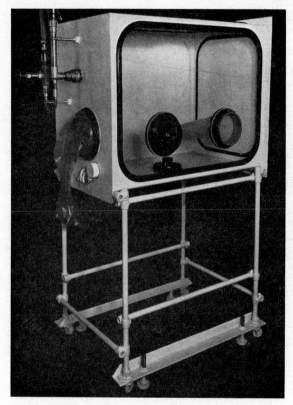

Figure 12.1. Glove box
(From *Glove Boxes and Shielded Cells* (Ed. Walton): Butterworths, London, 1958)
(By courtesy of United Kingdom Atomic Energy Authority)

emergency repairs at an atomic factory may have to be carried out by relays of men, each working for a few minutes.

(*c*) *Shield it*—Alpha particles are stopped by a thickness of paper or a surgical rubber glove, beta particles by a few mm of glass or Perspex (*Figure 12.1*). Gamma rays are greatly reduced in intensity by a few inches of lead or a few feet of concrete, water, or earth. Laboratory operations with gamma sources at curie levels are

181

often carried out behind a 4 in. thick wall of interlocking lead bricks (*Figure 12.2*). The necessary mechanical motions are done with special tongs which are carried through swivelling balls set in the wall, and the work is seen through windows which are constructed of 8 in. thick slabs of a lead oxide glass. The handling of

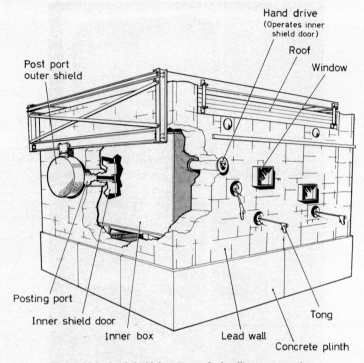

Figure 12.2. Lead-shielded equipment for handling gamma emitters
(From *Glove Boxes and Shielded Cells* (Ed. Walton): Butterworths, London, 1958)
(By courtesy of United Kingdom Atomic Energy Authority)

hundreds or thousands of curies is performed behind 3 ft. or more of concrete, with 'master-slave manipulators' which provide mechanical linkages between the motion of a control grip, outside the concrete barrier, and a working clamp inside the barrier. The work is seen through large glass tanks filled with a concentrated solution of zinc bromide, which are about as effective as the concrete in reducing the intensity of the gamma radiation.

(*d*) *Keep it out*—The precautions outlined above relate mainly to gamma radiation, that is they are concerned with avoiding any significant *external* radiation. It is equally necessary to avoid internal radiation from radioactive substances which threaten to become incorporated. We have seen on p. 171 that alpha, and to a lesser extent beta, sources are particularly dangerous inside the human body.

These materials are usually placed inside a 'glove box' (*Figure 12.1*), which is a totally enclosed miniature laboratory constructed of Perspex and metal or fibre-glass and provided with rubber gauntlets, sealed to portholes. Radiochemical laboratories and nuclear factories require high standards of ventilation and of general cleanliness in order that radioactive dust or gas is not allowed to accumulate in the air which is breathed by the workers. Smoking, eating, drinking, glassblowing, pipetting by mouth and the application of cosmetics are usually prohibited within laboratories and other areas where radioactive contamination could occur—this is to avoid breathing or swallowing such impurities.

MEASUREMENT

The success or otherwise of the above methods for avoiding excessive amounts of radiation can be monitored by dosimetry for external radiation and by bioassay for internal radiation.

(*a*) *Dosimetry*—The integrated dose of beta, of gamma and (with certain refinements of technique) of neutron radiation received by an individual can be measured if he has consistently worn a 'pocket ionization chamber' or a 'film badge'. The latter (*Figure 12.3*) depends on the blackening of a photographic film, which is revealed upon its subsequent development, and can be compared against standards. The film badge, and a subsequent developing and reporting service, can be obtained from the Radiological Protection Service, Downs Hospital, Cotswold Road, Sutton, Surrey. It is commonly used to measure low dose rates of up to a few rem per year. The higher doses that might be received in a nuclear accident, or in war, can be measured with an ionization chamber or by following the effect on certain chemical reactions, e.g. the radiation-induced oxidation of ferrous salts to ferric salts.

(*b*) *Bioassay*—Radioactive impurities lodged in the body can, in certain cases, be detected and measured by 'whole body radiation monitors' in which gamma radiation or bremsstrahlung* which escapes from the body is caught by an assembly of large sodium iodide (or other suitable) scintillation detectors. Again, an indirect assay can be made by testing samples of blood, faeces or urine. A small

---

* Electromagnetic radiation which is emitted in low yield when beta particles are slowed down in an absorber.

fraction of the radioactive element leaves the body in the urine—unfortunately the rate of removal, although adequate for sensitive analytical techniques, is often insufficient to alleviate the harmful

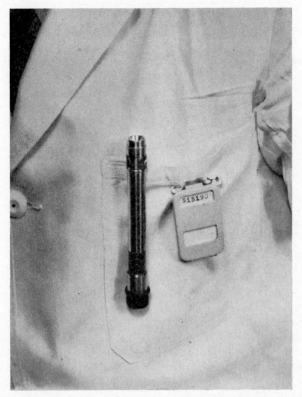

Figure 12.3. Photographic film badge and pocket ionization chamber, worn on the laboratory coat of an atomic scientist
(By courtesy of United Kingdom Atomic Energy Authority)

effects of internal radiation. Elements such as radium and plutonium become fixed in the skeletal system and there is no proved method of removing them within the lifetime of the patient.

APPENDIX
SUGGESTIONS FOR FURTHER STUDY

Chapter

1   *Madame Curie.* Eve Curie. (1938). London; Heinemann; (1962). Mercury Books.

2–4   *Radiations from Radioactive Substances.* Sir Ernest Rutherford, James Chadwick and C. D. Ellis. (1930). Cambridge University Press.

6   *The Story of Atomic Energy.* Frederick Soddy. (1949). London; Nova Atlantis.

  Pioneer Research on the Atom. Muriel Howorth. (1958). London; New World Publications.

  Chart of the Nuclides. J. R. Stehn and E. F. Clancy, G. E. C., Knolls Laboratory, U.S.A.

7   *Introduction to Atomic Physics.* S. Tolansky. (1956). London; Longmans, 4th ed.

8   *Atoms in the Family.* Laura Fermi. (1955). London; Allen and Unwin.

9   *Sourcebook on Atomic Energy.* Samuel Glasstone. (1958). Princeton, New Jersey; Van Nostrand.

  Atomic Energy for Military Purposes. Henry D. Smyth. (1948). Princeton University Press.

  Brighter than 1000 Suns. Robert Jungk. (1960). London; Penguin.

  Textbook of Reactor Physics. J. F. Hill. (1961). London; Allen and Unwin.

  Nuclear Power, Today and Tomorrow. Kenneth Jay. (1961). London; Methuen.

10   *Chemical Processing of Nuclear Fuels.* F. S. Martin and G. L. Miles. (1958). London; Butterworths.

  Radiochemical Studies: The Fission Products. Ed. Charles D. Coryell and Nathan Sugarman, Books 1, 2 and 3. (McGraw-Hill, New York, National Nuclear Energy Series, Division IV, Volume 9).

  The Chemistry of the Actinide Elements. Joseph J. Katz and Glenn T. Seaborg. (1957). London; Methuen.

11   *Isotopes.* J. L. Putman. (1960). London; Penguin.

  'Radioactivation Analysis' (a Review Article). E. N. Jenkins and A. A. Smales. *Quarterly Reviews of the Chemical Society of London.* (1956). Vol. X, No. 1.

  Radioisotope Laboratory Techniques. R. A. Faires and B. H. Parks. (1960). London; Newnes.

12   *Atomic Radiation and Life.* Peter Alexander. (1957). London; Penguin.

  Radiations and Living Cells. F. G. Spear. (1953). London; Chapman and Hall.

  Radiation and Health. Katharine Williams, C. L. Smith and H. D. Chalke. (1962). London; Longmans.

AN INTRODUCTION TO RADIOACTIVITY

Work in schools must use low activity levels and relatively low voltage equipment to comply with *Ministry of Education Administration Memorandum 577* of 24 October 1958. A useful source of information on equipment, some of which can be made in school workshops is:

Radioactivity Measuring Instruments. M. C. Nokes. (1956). London; Heinemann.

Radioactive sources can be prepared from a few grammes of a uranium or of a thorium salt. Even short-lived sources (for the demonstration of half-life) could be prepared in this way, for example:

thorium-234 ($t_{\frac{1}{2}} = 24\cdot1$ days) and protactinium-234 ($t_{\frac{1}{2}} = 1\cdot18$ min) from uranium salts.

bismuth-212 ($t_{\frac{1}{2}} = 60\cdot5$ min), radium-224 ($t_{\frac{1}{2}} = 3\cdot6$ days), lead-212 ($t_{\frac{1}{2}} = 10\cdot6$ h) from thorium salts.

Demonstrations of experiments which use higher levels of activity and specialized equipment are best seen on film or at special lecture demonstrations organized by the U.K.A.E.A., the Royal Institution, the Royal Institute of Chemistry or similar bodies; e.g. 'Radioactivity', a film for schools, produced by ICI Film Unit in collaboration with W. Ashhurst, F. Inst.P. (Epsom College) and E. N. Jenkins, with laboratory demonstrations by A. J. Wood (U.K.A.E.A.), and 'Radioactive Elements: A lecture demonstration for sixth form science students' by E. N. Jenkins and A. J. Wood, AERE-L138 (H.M. Stationery Office, London, 1962).

AUTHOR INDEX

187

SUBJECT INDEX

Acceleration of charged particles, 88–90
Actinide series, 138, 149–50
Actinium, 7, 149
Age of the earth, 158
Alpha,
  decay, mechanism of, 84
  energies, 17
  particle, 9–23
    biological effects, 171–2
    electrical charge, 18, 20, 21
    electrical deflection, 20
    magnetic deflection, 19
    mass, 21
    rays, 7
    spectrum, 16
Aluminium,
  absorption curve, 25, 155, 164–5
  bombardment by alpha particles, 90
Americium, 129, 145, 149
Amersham, 161–2, 166
Ammonium,
  α-hydroxy isobutyrate, 137
  pertechnetate, 140
Anaemia, 173
Anion exchange resin, 134
Argonne National Laboratory, 145
Arsenic,
  bombardment by neutrons, 100
  trace analysis, 163–4
Artificial radioactivity, 85–100
Atomic batteries, 153
Atomic bombs, 126–7
Atomic number, 70–72
Atomic theory (of Dalton), 67
Associated Electrical Industries Ltd,
  154

Background radiation, 172, 179–80
Barium-137, 45
Barium-140, 40, 160–1
Barn, 96
Benzene hexachloride, 153
BEPO, 163
Berkelium, 145–7, 149
Beta,
  decay, mechanism of, 84
  particle, 24–33
    absorption in Al, 24–25, 155
    biological effects, 171–2
    electrical charge, 30
    electrical deflection, 30–31
    ionization due to, 26–27

Beta, particle (*cont.*)
    magnetic deflection, 28–31
    range, 24–26
    rays, 7
    spectrum, 31–33
Berkeley,
  California, 144
  Gloucestershire, 122–3
Beryllium, bombardment by alpha
    particles, 91–93
Binding energy, 36
Bioassay, 183–4
Biological effects of radioactivity, 169–
    84
Biological shield, 122
Bismuth-214, 19
Blanket, 125
Book of Isaiah, 160
Boron-10, 126
Bradwell, 122
Bremsstrahlung, 25, 183
Breeder reactor, 125–6
Burn-up of nuclear fuel, 123–4

Cadmium, control rods, 120–1
Caesium-137, 45, 130, 132, 142, 154
Calder Hall, 122
Californium, 145–6, 149
Cancer, 169–70
Capture   cross-section   in   uranium,
    111–12
Carbon cycle, 159
Carbon-14, 159, 166–8
Carrier, 61, 90, 134, 164
Carrier-free, 161
Cathode rays, 2–3
Central Electricity Generating Board,
    121–3
Cerium, 130, 134, 137
Cerium-141 and -144, 129, 130
Chain reaction, 108, 118–21
Chemical aspects of radioactive change,
    56–66
Chicago, 120–1
Chromosomes, 174–6
Citrate buffer, 135–7
Cloud chamber, 13–15, 25–26, 92
Cobalt-60, 35, 151, 153–5
Codes of practice, 180
Coefficient of variation, 49
Collective or unified model, 83–84, 117
Compound nucleus, 84, 104, 112, 114